THE DECOY MAN

the
DECOY MAN

The Extraordinary Adventures of an
Undercover Cop

by Charles Whited

PyP

A Playboy Press Book

Published simultaneously in the United States and Canada by Playboy Press, Chicago, Illinois. Printed in the United States of America. Library of Congress Catalog Card Number: 73-84921. Second Printing.

PLAYBOY and Rabbit Head design are trademarks of Playboy, 919 North Michigan Avenue, Chicago, Illinois 60611 (U.S.A.), Reg. U.S. Pat. Off., marca registrada, marque déposée.

Prologue

The guy was dead. Once he had lived and breathed, laughed and cursed and cried, loved and hated and felt cold. Now he was a blob of stinking remains in a rubber sack, and nobody gave a damn. Even we decoy men had held our noses, and, except for the neighborhood pusher, we had been closer to him than anybody because he had been our best squeal. They would bury him somewhere in a county grave, without even a stone to say, "Here Lies a Junkie, R.I.P."

Well, who would believe it? The pusher was judge, jury and executioner, all in one, and went about his business of murder with no need for proof and no more concern than if he'd swatted a fly. How cheap can human life be in the streets of a city? Even living the incident, as I did, the grisly business was hard to swallow. But then, there were a lot of episodes that seemed too bizarre to be real, things you will read about in this book.

Looking back now, to that period of my life as a decoy cop for the New York Police Department, much of it seems like a wild dream. And yet it was something I had to do. Dan Chiodo, ex-salesman, ex-businessman, ex-cargo manager, was living a boyhood dream to be a cop, loaded with idealism, authority and guts. Yessir, Dan Chiodo would help change the world, help rid it of hoods and punks, help make the streets safe again.

But you learn bitter truths in life, and I guess this is true of everybody. You learn that one man might as well try to stop a train by standing on the track. One man? Hell, the job in New York seemed too big for a whole police department of 28,000 men! For in the streets of the city, crime has become a way of life. And strange as it may seem, every law-abiding man, woman and child lives with the calculated risk of being a potential victim of crime.

Something terrible is happening. We're letting our society, or at least great segments of it, go to rot. There are two kinds of people who seem to be most aware of this: police officers and criminals. Other people read about it in their daily newspapers, make noises of shock and dismay, perhaps even offer half-hearted solutions. But the cop goes on living his anger and frustrations, day after day, and the criminal goes on with his mayhem and murder, day after day, and the rest of us simply take our calculated risks. And that's why this book, *The Decoy Man*, was written.

As an ex-cop, now in the real-estate business in Miami, I'm often astonished at the public's blithe acceptance of crime in American life. But then, even I was unprepared for the realities of it. Working as a decoy man, I often found myself thinking, "I can't believe this is happening. People aren't this brutal, they aren't this insensitive." And then, after a while, I began to reflect upon the great majority of people going about their ordinary lives. Could they have any idea of what was happening, every day and every night, within a few blocks of their own thresholds? Would they be shocked if they knew? Could they conceive of some of their own kids living as we decoys sometimes found them, camping in abandoned tenements with a stash of drugs, cutting holes in the floor as booby traps, so that if a cop barged in he might fall through and die?

On the job I began keeping records: memo books of my daily patrols, arrest cards, FBI rap sheets and special reports, giving dates, locations and details. All were methodically filed and kept safe.

I left the police department after nearly two-and-a-half years of some of the most concentrated violence and experience a man can stomach. I left more cynical about bureaucratic systems and more aware of the frailty of the ordinary citizen and his dependence on good cops. I went into business and, in time, came to Miami, where the sun is warm and the air cleaner. Some might say I gave up in despair and ran away from the problem. Maybe I did. Or maybe there is no place, really, left to run. Whatever the reason, I'm out of it physically, but mentally I'll never be out of it entirely. Once you've lived in the jungle, its memory never leaves you.

People have asked, "What do you want this book to say? What is its message?" A better understanding, perhaps, of the cop and his role in society, and why he thinks and acts the way he does. If it merely makes you a little more tolerant the next time a cop asks for your driver's license, something will have been achieved.

Some people will read this book with mixed feelings. Some may praise and some condemn. And there are also those who will say, "Yeah, I remember Chi. He wasn't so tough." Or, "Yeah, he was a tough, crazy guinea." Or, "Chiodo was a bull-shit artist, always telling stories."

Anybody who becomes involved in a book, whether it's written by him or about him, has debts of gratitude to acknowledge. I feel that I must extend thanks to many people, but especially to certain members of the New York Police Department and to Bill Kofoed, a young Miami public-relations man who encouraged me to tell these stories. It was through him and his father

Jack, a columnist for the *Miami Herald,* that I met writer Charles Whited.

The events are true, as I saw them and lived them, and are backed up by my notes, memo books and police records. We've changed the names of people involved, including my partners, for obvious reasons. But incidents such as these are part of the daily police records of cities, large and small, all over this country. Some people may say that this is not a "nice" book, and will regard certain language and characters as offensive. But the story is told as it happened, using the language of the street. We are writing about real people, and some of the things they do and say may shock the sensibilities of those who block out the seamy side of life. And yet such things affect all of us, good citizens and bad. It may be time for the sensitive to be more open-minded, not merely to the acceptable side of life but also to the cruel, wanton and insensitive side. Only by recognizing what exists can we start joining together for meaningful change and a better world.

The Decoy Man tells it like it is. The guys in the station houses will understand.

Dan Chiodo, Miami, Florida, 1973

1

Shield 27996

The evening was hot and muggy. Even the ocean breeze gave no relief. Sweat trickled down Chiodo's forehead, soaking the inner band of his riot helmet. He felt uncomfortably conspicuous in the stiff new uniform, with the shiny shield on his chest, the nightstick dangling from his new gunbelt. They were pacing Post Seven of the 60th Precinct, Coney Island. An hour before, the man beside him, Patrolman Dave Cassino, had been a name on a roster in the squad room. "Cassino-Chiodo, Post 7." Now he was a flesh-and-blood partner and a voice in the gathering darkness.

". . . Hot for some action, right, kid? Three weeks in the academy and busting to make an arrest?"

Chiodo nodded.

"Let me tell you something, kid. When you work with me you don't see nothing unless I see it. If I don't see nothing, you don't see nothing. I ain't gonna haul you out of no bullshit."

The man had an angular, weathered face and crow's-feet

around the eyes. His gunbelt was old, his shield darkened around the indentations, his trousers shiny in the seat. A deep scratch curved down the left side of his helmet, and the chin strap was frayed from many wearings. Beneath the helmet, his hair was kinky and gray. But under the gunbelt Dave Cassino had no paunch. At 41 he was sinewy and tough.

For Chiodo, Daniel J., Shield No. 27996, the change had come with stunning speed. Just three weeks before, he was standing his first formation in the Police Academy.

"This is the largest class in the history of the New York Police Department," the instructor had told them. "We don't have enough shields for all of you. Those men who do not receive their shields will have to wait." It took ten days for all 860 rookies to pin them on. In another week, on July 1, 1968, they were ordered out on the streets.

It was an unprecedented move by the city, but New York was in crisis. There was trouble in Harlem, trouble in Brooklyn, trouble in Coney Island, even trouble in Times Square, and the summer was just beginning to heat up. City Hall was scraping the barrel to put blue-uniformed bodies on the streets. The public clamored for police, and more police.

"This is your first night out, ain't it?"

Chiodo hated to admit it, but the question had to come sooner or later. Yes, this was his first night out. "They picked sixty of us for TPF. There were a lot more volunteers."

Cassino grunted.

The words of the assistant commander, Tactical Patrol Force, came back to Chiodo. The assistant commander had stood before them in a sparkle of brass, speaking like a sales manager at the morning pep meeting.

"You men are on temporary assignment to the finest police unit in the world. The TPF is an elite team. When there's action, you can damn well expect to be in the middle of it, because that's what you are here for. You will be prepared to move at a moment's notice anywhere in this city. And you are

2

not always going to be welcomed by the local precinct personnel. Some of them will hate your guts because you are TPF. That's their can of worms, not yours. Now, you rookies stick close to those older partners. They know the ropes. Watch them, listen to them and don't give them any lip. As for you older men—" he turned to a group of police veterans whose uniform collars blazed with the silver TPF insignia "—sometimes I've got to admit you get a little overeager to make arrests and make a name for yourselves. I've been getting reports of guys tossing coins to see who gets the collar. I don't have to tell you how bad this sounds in court. Whoever's the arresting officer is the arresting officer. Don't be tossing coins in front of the criminal. . . ."

Tossing coins to make arrests. This was the kind of outfit to be in; and here he was walking Surf Avenue, a curious and sometimes violent blending ground of humanity in Coney Island, sweating under his helmet, the nightstick slapping his thigh. But was this what he really wanted? He was not sure.

"It's good duty, kid," Cassino was saying. "Hours are good. They brief you on the hours?"

"Yeah. Six to two, four nights a week and two days off. That gives you eighteen extra days off a year, right?"

"Right. Me, I've been able to keep a part-time business going. If I don't make a late collar and have to go to court next morning, I can get to work by ten o'clock easy."

"What kind of business have you got?"

"Grocery store in the Bronx. Me and the wife run it. TPF hours work out real good. Other guys work all kinds of extra jobs. We've got insurance men, clerks, guys that work the racetrack, guys going full time to NYU. A buddy of mine got his law degree last month."

"This helmet's hot."

"You'll get used to it. Got to wear them on this post. Sometimes stuff comes off the rooftops. You can get brained with a brick and never see who dropped it."

"You get a lot of arrests, Cassino?"

"Me? Naw, I ain't had a collar in four months."

"But I thought . . ."

"That's the trouble with you rookies. You think too much."

The talk died. Chiodo listened to their footfalls on the pavement, mixing with the sounds of passing traffic, the life of the neighborhood, distant laughter and shouts. They passed a man and woman embracing on the stoop of a tenement. Cassino nudged him.

"That's one of the fringe benefits, kid. Broads. Some broads get hot just being near the uniform. I've seen 'em walk right up and grab you between the legs. That makes it nice, because most cops I know are naturally horny bastards anyhow. Screw anything in a skirt. Like that old joke about the dead body they found in an alley. Cop calls in to the desk lieutenant and says, 'Hey, lou, there's a dead cop in the alley.' Lieutenant says, 'What's his name?' The guy says, 'Damned if I know. No identification and not a stitch on him.' The lou says, 'How do you know he's a cop?' The guy says, 'Because he's got a hard-on and coffee running out his ears.' "

As Cassino broke into an explosive guffaw, a car pulled over to the curb, and the driver, a fat, middle-aged man, tooted his horn. "Hey, officers, some cops are having trouble down at the beach."

"Okay, give us a lift."

Two uniformed TPF men were standing on the boardwalk talking with a lifeguard. The lifeguard was gesturing toward a crowd of Puerto Rican youths. Cassino and Chiodo arrived running. "What's the trouble?"

"Some spic pulled a knife on this lifeguard," said a tall TPF man. "He's over in that crowd. There's about forty of them, I figure. This guy wants to press charges."

"You bet your ass I want to press charges," said the lifeguard.

"The guy was probably only fooling around," said the tall TPF man.

4

"Bullshit," said the lifeguard.

"Well, we'll have to go in and take the kid."

The tall TPF man moved toward the group. Chiodo started to follow, but Cassino caught his sleeve. "No, kid. One man goes in, the rest of us stay out. That way we're set to make a rush if he needs help."

Silently the crowd parted for the tall TPF man, and he confronted a lean, shaggy-haired Puerto Rican. "Hey, you," said the tall TPF man, jabbing his finger. "You got a knife?"

"Yeah."

"Did you chase that lifeguard with a knife?"

"Yeah."

"All right, hands on your head and come with me. You're under arrest."

With a shrug, the Puerto Rican obeyed. The crowd made no move to interfere. A quick search yielded a switchblade from his back pocket. As the prisoner stood sullenly, handcuffed behind his back, the tall TPF man said, "Okay, who wants the collar?"

"Don't look at me," said his partner.

"Me neither," Cassino said. "You guys are partners, you settle it."

"I sure as hell don't want it," said the tall TPF man. He fished in his pocket and brought out a quarter. "Odd man?"

"I'll take the collar," said Chiodo. They turned as if noticing his presence for the first time. Experienced eyes flicked to his bare collar. There was a shaking of heads.

"You're a rookie. Rookies don't make arrests."

The two partners flipped. "Heads," said the tall TPF man. The quarter came up heads. "Hah, I win," said the tall TPF man. "You take the collar."

Later, as they again walked Post Seven, Chiodo puzzled over the coin flipping. It wasn't what he had expected.

"Hey, Cassino, that ain't the way the assistant commander described this gung-ho TPF outfit in his speech."

5

Cassino smirked. "Kid . . ."

"Yeah?"

"You got a lot to learn."

It was true. He had a lot to learn. Part of it was simply learning routine, but routine settled in quickly enough. During the day he had time to idle about the house in Queens with Linda and the two children, work out in the academy gym and study his manuals. In just three weeks of formal training, he felt acutely his ignorance of laws and evidence, apprehension of suspects, fingerprinting, radio procedure, first aid, administrative forms and the thousand-and-one other details of police work. Before returning to duty from days off, he would call TPF headquarters for the next night's assignment.

"This is Patrolman Chiodo, Squad Three-D. Where are we working tomorrow night?"

The clerk would flip through his roster sheets. "Yeah, tomorrow night the Third Squad is at the Six-Oh." That was Coney Island. Sometimes the assignment was Brooklyn or Manhattan South or, on rare occasions, Queens. At 5:45 P.M. he would arrive at the station house, jot down in his memo book the ten most recent alarms and get the name of his partner for the evening off the bulletin board. At six o'clock the sergeant would walk into the squad room. "Okay, guys, let's fall in for roll call. Adams, Johnson, Post Nine. Radio two-seven-one-three. Adams, meal at eight, Johnson at ten. . . ."

Each week the partners and posts varied. Older men shared scraps of police gossip and tricks of the trade. There were those who took free meals and cigarettes and those who did not, those who sneaked a nip on duty and those who never touched the stuff in uniform, those who spent their evening meal break with a woman and those who were staunch family men.

One evening in Brooklyn, his partner's portable Motorola crackled. "Mobilization! Squad Two, mobilization!" They sprinted two blocks to the station house, grabbed helmets and riot sticks from the trunks of their cars and piled into the big green bus as it pulled away.

"What the fuck's going on?"

"Got some firemen in trouble. Niggers sniping from the roofs."

It was a warehouse blaze, ignited by gasoline bombs. Flames enveloped the 12-story building and showered sparks into the street. From deep inside the inferno came muffled booms. Fire hoses twisted through wet streets, and the flames silhouetted men manning hoses from towering ladders. On the ground, firemen crouched beside their engines as tiny puffs of concrete burst around them. Before the TPF bus stopped rolling, the doors snapped open and helmeted men were pouring out. "Move your asses!" bawled a sergeant.

A white-helmeted fire chief was pointing at the rooftop of a brick tenement half a block away, shouting something. Chiodo followed the line of scurrying men and looked up. Pinpoints of light winked like fireflies along the tenement parapet. The line stopped, crouched along the fire engines and in the shelter of parked cars. Around him Chiodo heard what sounded like fire-crackers going off. Policemen were returning pistol fire, steadying their aims with both hands. Chiodo squatted by the fender of a white Chevy, aiming his .38 high and squeezing off the shots. The sharp odor of cordite bit into his nostrils. Along the black roofline, the fireflies went out.

The squad deployed in a line along the street, and small groups of TPF men were detailed to continue sporadic pistol fire at the rooftops. Beside one of the fire engines a young, blond-haired fireman was receiving first aid for a gunshot wound in the foot. The white bandage was in stark contrast to the slick black boots, coats and helmets of the firemen. A policeman came down the TPF line with a bucket of cold water. Chiodo drank deeply from the metal cup, washing his parched tongue and throat. He had never been so thirsty.

Half an hour later, Chiodo and 19 others climbed back into the bus and returned to the station. They were wet, sooty and tired. No one spoke until the doors opened and they began to unload. Chiodo grinned at his partner for the evening, a bluff, profane Irishman named Barney.

"They can't do this to me, Barney. I'm still a fucking rookie."

"You *were* a fucking rookie," Barney said. "Now you're a fucking combat soldier." He pulled a cigarette from a crumpled pack, snapped a lighter, and smoke billowed around his broad, freckled face. "I shoulda listened to my mother. Do you know what she wanted me to be?"

"What?"

"A priest."

He liked Barney. They had things in common. Years before, as boys, they had lived in rival neighborhoods in Brooklyn, but had not met until now. "I wonder if you're the redheaded bastard I hit in the face with a carpet gun?" Chiodo said.

"Naw, that must have been some other redheaded bastard," Barney laughed.

Over coffee they talked of the old days. Their routes into police work had been surprisingly similar, probably because many kids in the neighborhood shared the same ambition. It was a middle-class part of Brooklyn, and families tended to stay together. In another part of New York, such as the heavily Sicilian parts of the Lower East Side, things might have been different.

The Catholic Chiodos had lived in a complex of apartment buildings surrounded by Jewish families. His friends were named Goldberg and Rubin and Epstein. Across the avenue were the Irish, and a natural rivalry flared between them. The Irish kids would cross the avenue brandishing carpet guns. Fitted with a heavy rubber band that propelled a square of linoleum, the crude weapon could knock out an eye. Sometimes the gangs met with sticks and ball bats and fought until the blood flowed. Chiodo's Sicilian temper made up for his lack of bulk, for he was tall and skinny and usually outweighed.

"You must not have stayed in the neighborhood," Barney said. "We'd have run into each other sooner or later."

8

"We moved out when I was fourteen, over to City Line. The kids there had softball teams instead of gangs, but sometimes they'd take off the softball uniforms and put on the garrison belts with the big metal studs. Remember them? You'd wrap the belt around your hand and flail away," Chiodo said.

"What about the cosa nostra? I guess you met a lot of those families?" Barney said.

Chiodo shook his head. "A lot of people ask me that. It's a funny thing. The mafia didn't exist for me, growing up. Such things just weren't discussed at home. Looking back, I can't remember anything negative being discussed. When I first found out there was an underworld and that Sicilians were involved, it hit me like a bomb. So my dad would say, 'There's good and bad in everybody.' Mom would tell stories about certain men on the Lower East Side who were feared when her parents lived there. 'But you mind your own business and don't bother them,' she would say, 'and they won't bother you.' When she was a child, her family lived on Fountain Avenue in Brooklyn. You know, near the Old Mill. Some people say the place was a dumping ground for Murder, Incorporated. They'd find bodies in there, guys with concrete shoes. But my folks kept my sisters and me shielded from such memories. You might say we lived in a vacuum. Nothing bad ever happened. Italians were the greatest people on earth, and if you weren't Catholic you were doomed."

"My mother was disappointed when I went into police work," Barney said. "I've got two uncles who are cops. But she was real religious, and I think it was her life's ambition to have a son in the priesthood."

Chiodo stared into his coffee cup. "Yeah, my folks weren't overjoyed either." Fatigue from the evening's exertions washed over him. It felt good to rest and talk. He lit a cigarette and remembered how bitter his father had been.

At 18 Chiodo had enrolled at NYU part time and got a job at the airport. His father lectured him about the future, brown

9

eyes snapping. "You make something of yourself, Dan. Don't be a bum." John Chiodo was the son of an immigrant and worked on a city garbage truck; he wanted better for his only son. The job at the airport was good, but Chiodo left it for six months of active duty in the Army Reserve. When that was ended he started his own trucking business. At 21 he married Linda in a big Italian wedding, with a band, two halls and 360 guests. Then they took an apartment in Queens.

He could never pinpoint when the idea of becoming a policeman had been ignited. At times he doubted the wisdom of it.

Periodically the ads had appeared in the papers announcing new police examinations. The ads nagged at him. "I'm going to take the test," he told Linda. On the first test he made 97. But he could not bring himself to go the next step, the physical examination. He knew his eyesight was poor. Besides, he had sold the trucking business and gotten a job with Seaboard World Airlines, first in sales and later as a cargo manager. By the age of 25 he had a good future and was making $13,000 a year. They talked of opening a branch in San Francisco, and he knew that he was being considered to manage it. Then Mayor Lindsay gave in to the public outcry for more cops, and the police department launched a big recruitment drive.

"Linda," he said, "I'm going to take the test."

"What, again? Why?"

"I don't know, I'm just taking it."

There were conflicts inside him. Newspaper accounts of policemen being beaten, of rapists being set free, of monsters prowling the streets frustrated and galled him. "If I was a cop . . ." he told himself. He was troubled, too, by scandals of dishonesty, laziness and corruption among policemen. But how could he moralize and yet do nothing? "If people like me don't do anything, then we're to blame," he tried to tell Linda. "I don't want to be to blame."

And yet, was he being too selfish? Their children, Diane and Lisa, were four and five years old. Was he cheating them and

Linda out of the things money would buy? What of the future? On the night before the tests, he had gotten drunk. The next morning, head aching and mouth cottony, he had gone to Jefferson High School with two friends and his cousin, Big Pete. With 800 police jobs to be filled, the line stretched for blocks. They pushed their way to the front and were the last to get inside. Moments later, the angry crowd outside rioted.

For the fourth time he passed the mental examination. But this time he also went for the physical. Months passed before the notice came in the mail to report to the Police Academy on June 23. Chiodo had just returned from a business trip to Frankfurt, Zurich and London for Seaboard Airlines. He read the notice and whooped, "I've been accepted!" Linda shook her head. "You've got to be out of your mind."

The airline's traffic vice-president felt the same way. "Are you serious? You want to be a cop?" Chiodo nodded. "As soon as we open in San Francisco, you've got that manager's job," the vice-president said. "Don't you understand that? Do you want to take a pay cut, become one of the crowd? Why?"

"Well, I want to go back to college," Chiodo said lamely. "I can't work here and go to college, too."

"Look, we'll send you to college and I'll see what I can do to get the company to pay for it."

"I've got to give it a try."

The vice-president looked grave.

There were 860 of them in the class. Processing was incomplete. They were issued gray cadet uniforms and guns. So hastily had the huge muster been put together that one man's background check would later reveal that he was a wanted felon. Another would shoot his wife in a drunken brawl.

Chiodo plunged into a crowded schedule of lectures, orientation classes and physical training in the gym. He lugged home books on law, search and seizure and the rights of suspects. The weather was warm, and riots brewed in isolated pockets of the city. New York was in the grip of street crime, and the blue line stretched thin. The order came down to put every available man on the streets. Three weeks after starting in the academy, the first contingent of rookies was mobilized. Chiodo requested assignment to the Tactical Patrol Force, New York's fast-moving force of shock troops trained in mob control and culled from the cream of academy recruits.

The newspapers made much of the TPF as its highly mobile squads swept into high-crime areas against muggers, mashers and robbers. But in the process they also grabbed litterbugs, jaywalkers and people involved in family quarrels. Such unblinking impartiality galled petty law violators and incensed old-line precinct cops. Students and civil-rights demonstrators cried, "Gestapo!" In a city where small-time graft among some 28,000 policemen was a way of life, ranging from free meals to protection payoffs, incorruptible law enforcement came as a shock. Grumbled a lieutenant in Brooklyn: "Every time I hear they're being sent into my precinct, I know I'll be writing up arrest reports all night. They'll arrest anybody. They're all looking for big, fat arrest quotas."

If the arrival of uniformed TPF squads in a neighborhood wasn't worrisome enough, the presence of their decoy units— undercover teams blending inconspicuously into the life of the street—was even worse. Just as the 1000-member TPF regarded itself as the élite of New York's police, the decoy men regarded themselves as the cream of the TPF. Hunting down the hoodlum on his own ground, they upset the status quo, often overrode local authority and thumbed their noses at the rules.

A TPF lieutenant scanned Chiodo's academy file. "Good test score," he mused. "You're ranking in the top fifty. Background check? Yes. Hmmm. Okay, Chiodo, your temporary assignment is TPF. . . ."

There had been bad scenes with his parents. His father's face darkened and the brown eyes flashed. "You're crazy, you don't wanna be no cop," John Chiodo said. "The trouble with cops, they're getting killed, beat up, spit on. It's a lousy life. Years ago

12

when people were starving and couldn't get no jobs, that was different. When you was lucky to eat once a week, a cop had a better deal. Besides, people respected him. It ain't that way no more, son. Go back to the airport, make something out of yourself."

Chiodo stood firm. "I'm going to give it a try."

His father threw up his hands. "All right, try. Do what you want to do."

"Why you want to do that?" his mother began. "It's dangerous. Isn't it dangerous? I know a lot of people got sons and nephews who are cops and they don't like it. And when you finish, it'll be hard to get a good job again."

"Don't worry, mom—"

"You always say don't worry. Don't worry. That's your middle name, don't worry. All your life you say don't worry."

He began to dread going to his folks' house for Sunday dinner. Linda felt the same way. After dinner, as they sat and smoked, his father would start. "What are you gonna do about it?"

"About what?"

"This stupid job. You know what happened in Harlem the other night? Cop got shot. Kid younger than you, he got shot in the back. You ain't going to keep that job, are you?"

"Yeah, dad, I'm going to keep it."

"Boy, you're stupid. I used to think you was smart, but you're stupid. Look, if you want a civil-service job why don't you get in the sanitation department like me? Our benefits are better."

"Police make more money. Six hundred dollars more."

"Six hundred dollars!" John Chiodo snorted. "Big deal, when your life is on the line."

"I'm going to be a good cop."

"You know, your father is really upset," his mother said.

"I'm sorry he's upset."

"Dan has got to live his own life," Linda said.

"He's your husband. You should care about him. Two small children to support and him giving up thirteen thousand at the

13

airport. And for what? He might wind up getting himself killed."

"A man has got to do what he's got to do," Linda said.

"Aren't you going to worry? He's got to work nights in this —this TP whatchamacallit and leave you home alone with the kids. I know my crazy son. He'll be locking up everybody and getting into trouble. What if he locks up somebody he ain't supposed to lock up?"

"Don't tell me how to be a cop or who I'm supposed to lock up," Dan snapped.

"Listen to that, will you? And I'm his mother. He's starting to talk like an animal."

The scenes hardened his resolve. All right, he would not only be a cop, he would try to be the best cop in the city of New York. And now, with temporary TPF duty assured, the time had come to test himself. . . .

Barney blew a smoke ring. The ring drifted lazily through the still air and broke apart on Chiodo's empty coffee cup. "Gonna be real gung-ho, huh?" Barney said, smiling. "A Sicilian super-cop." The stink of smoke was still in his uniform, and soot streaked his Irish face.

"Yeah. And you know what I'll do to any dumb Irishman that gets in my way?"

"What?"

"I'll get him in the head with my carpet gun."

2

"Halt, or I'll Shoot!"

"Hey, Chiodo, what squad they got you in?"

"Third squad, Brooklyn South."

"Uh-huh. Frank Mack's outfit. He's your sergeant. Good man. But let me give you some tips. . . ."

In the bleak anonymity of the old precinct station house, Dave Fraley's craggy face emerged as a pleasant surprise. He had been a boyhood acquaintance, and they were about the same age. But four years in the police department and the rank of detective gave Fraley an added maturity. Under his scrutiny Chiodo became even more conscious of the new blue uniform with its blank collar.

"I think I know how you feel, Dan. Want to go right out and start making arrests?"

"Right."

"Well, don't get your guinea blood up. Do you know what your status is right now in the New York Police Department? I'll tell you. A piece of lint on the captain's ass carries more weight. You're an academy probie, Dan. You've got seven months of probation ahead. Guys on probation shouldn't make waves, understand? Don't give no summonses, don't make arrests, don't do nothing. You see something happening, look the other way."

"What kind of bullshit is that, Dave?"

"No bullshit, these are facts of life, man. You're a real aggressive guy and I've seen that Sicilian temper flash. But I'm telling you straight. When you're on probation, don't do nothing. If you make an arrest and somebody files a complaint on you, the brass ain't going to take gaff from the public. They can throw you right off the job and not even give you a reason. And let me tell you something about Frank Mack. He likes to run his squad nice and tidy. Keep the paper work down and don't kick up dust, that's Mack. He's a good cop, but don't start getting involved because you'll piss him off. If you do something, anything, he's got to write a report and file it with the Police Academy, TPF headquarters and God knows where else. Frank just don't like to be bothered. . . ."

"That's his problem, Dave."

"No, Dan. That's your problem. Just listen to me and stay out of trouble. There are plenty of collars out on the street. They'll still be there when you're no longer on probation."

Masking his nervousness, Chiodo reported to the Third Squad for roll call. In the sitting room, the mood was loose and relaxed. As men waited for roll call, a burly veteran ambled over and sat down on a desk beside Chiodo.

"First night in the street, kid?"

"Not exactly. I worked a couple of nights in the six-oh precinct. This is my first night in eight-three."

"Hammond's my name. Gene Hammond."

"Hi, Gene. I'm Dan Chiodo."

"Hey, you're the rook I'm working with tonight."

"Is that so?"

"If you'd looked at the roster, you'd see we're working Post

39 in the eight-one. It's the worst post in the precinct. Some real bad-asses hang out on that post. But don't worry, kid, we'll take it nice and easy. I'm not no hero. I want to be around to collect my pension."

Chiodo caught a whiff of liquor as Hammond spoke. The eyes were a bit red-rimmed, but clear. Around them, men talked with gruff familiarity. Profanity sprinkled the stale air.

" . . . She's standing there screaming at me, 'Mr. Policeman, that son of a bitch threw my panties up on the telephone pole. Look, there they are. That bastard. What are you gonna do about it?' So I says, 'Lady, what the hell am I supposed to do? Climb up and get 'em?' . . ."

" . . . So I'd finished readin' the cat his rights. 'You got a right to remain silent. You got a right to a lawyer. If you ain't got no lawyer, a lawyer will be provided.' All that shit. The mother-fucker gets this smirk on his face and he says, 'You know what you is, brother? You a black pig. You an Uncle Tom.' He's just gettin' ready to spit in my face when this accident happened. His head accidentally runs into my nightstick. Fucker's out cold. The sergeant, he say, 'Jones, did you hit that man?' I say, 'Naw, sergeant, I didn't hit him. Do you think I'd hit a soul brother? That man fell down. . . .'"

"Chiodo, you're supposed to get in fifteen minutes before roll call. You check the roll and get all this shit on your memo book: post, partner, tour of duty, weather. Then get the ten latest GLAs off the hot sheet. Don't expect to get paid for that extra fifteen minutes, though. That's just something else the PBA lets this bullshit city get away with. Then if you get a radio, like tonight we'll get one—we better get one on that post—you better check it out before you leave the house, make sure the damn thing works. You don't always get a radio unless you're working a real bad post, and, man, tonight we drew the worst post in the city. Anyhow, in case of a mobilization you'll get word over the air. If you don't have a radio and there's a mobili-zation, a patrol car will come cruising along the post real slow

17

with his dome light flashing. When you see that, get your ass back to the house by any means available, and that includes flagging down a civilian car. You've got to be at the house ready to go in five minutes. Most times we're leaving some dumb jerk beh—"

"Let's go. Knock it off!" Sergeant Frank Mack, a thin, taciturn man, strode into the squad room carrying a clipboard. "Knock off the bullshit, I said. What are you guys, deaf?" The room quieted. "Okay, that's better. Tomorrow night the Third Squad's at the seven-one." There were groans from the ranks. "Okay, knock it off! Let's listen up. Asbury, McGrew, Post Ten. Asbury, meal at eight, McGrew ten . . . Chi-Chiodo, Hammond, Post 39, both take meal at nine. . . ."

As the sergeant continued roll call, Hammond muttered, "These guys are crazy. They don't like the Seven-one Precinct. No action, they say. Man, I'll take the Seventy-first over this jungle anytime. . . ."

"Hey, Hammond," shouted Mack. "You got all night to talk to that guy."

Post 39 drew a pocket-size Motorola radio. Chiodo picked it out of the rack and read off the number to Sergeant Mack. It was 2481. Hammond took the unit from his hand and they headed for the patrol car that would drop them off on Reid Avenue.

The slum brooded around them in the gathering dusk, its smells a mixture of decay, cooking odors, dank cracks between buildings, garbage and human excrement. As the police car drove away, Chiodo felt strangely alien, an intruder in a dark world. Black men and women watched from stoops and sagging iron fire escapes. The sidewalks and streets were cracked, pot-holed and strewn with garbage. Chunks of broken asphalt and cement littered their way. Between the narrow cement side-walk and the broken curbing stretched a foot-wide space of grassless dirt. Soul music drifted down from an open window. "Baby, baby, baby, looka here what you done this time. Baby,

baby . . ." Across the street a Jewish merchant snapped a padlock to the iron shutters of his shop and hurried to a waiting car. A sign over the shop read,

F. COHEN
RELIGIOUS ARTICLES
CHARMS

Hammond fiddled with the radio.

"Portable two-four-eight-one to eight-three base."

"Go ahead, two-four-eight-one."

"How do you read me?"

"Five by five."

"Ten-four."

There were five blocks to the post. The patrol was supposed to walk five blocks down one side of Reid Avenue, cross the street and walk five blocks back. Hammond was preoccupied and nervous. He walked slowly beside Chiodo, seldom speaking, eyes constantly shifting. Before they had covered four blocks, he had checked the radio three more times and the darkness had become complete. Many streetlights were broken, leaving great patches of deep shadow. At the end of the fourth block, Hammond turned and they headed back. Chiodo felt the weight of the .38 on his belt and the stick he carried in his left hand.

On the second pass, Hammond stopped at a tiny market. "Kid, how about a soda?" A frail Puerto Rican woman gave them two bottles and refused to take their money.

"These people are good to us that way," Hammond said.

Chiodo shrugged. "Yeah."

They stood drinking by the light of a single bulb hanging from the ceiling. Beads of sweat glistened on Hammond's upper lip, and his hand trembled. Chiodo suddenly realized that his partner was sick with fear.

Back on the street, Chiodo started toward the fifth block of their post. Hammond plucked at his arm. "Where you going, kid? Let's go back this way."

"Doesn't our post go to Lafayette Street?"

"Yeah, but you don't want to go down there, kid."

"Hey, why not go down to that end? We haven't completed our tour of the post yet."

Hammond shook his head and gave a nervous chuckle. "Down there's where the zoo is, kid. Nothing but wild apes, and we don't have no bananas to feed 'em."

"I'm going to have a look. You can wait here."

Hammond swallowed hard. "All right. But let me tell you something. There's a bar and poolhall on the corner and a bunch of bad people hang out there. When we walk by, we're gonna catch all kinds of shit. No matter what they say or do, don't turn around, don't talk back, don't do nothing."

As they neared the corner, the crowd loomed out of the shadows. Black youths lounged along the sidewalk drinking beer, smoking, talking. A lone streetlight illuminated the scene. As the light caught their uniforms, heads turned and eyes inspected them coolly. "Well, well," said a mocking voice, "what do we got here? Two honky pigs. Hey, pigs, give us an oink. Let's have us some roast pig. Hyah, hyah, hyah." Other voices chimed in. "Hey, motherfucker, we goin' to get your ass. What you doin' down here, honkies? This is soul country." A beer can sailed from the group and clattered to the sidewalk at Chiodo's feet.

"Hey," he shouted, "cut out that shit!"

Hammond grabbed his arm and steered him across the street. "I'm telling you, kid, cool it."

"But they can't pull that shit on us."

"Come on, let's move out of here."

Chiodo stopped and stared across the street. Blacks hooted and jeered. The crowd thickened as more came out of the bar to watch the excitement. "Yah! Yah! Fuckin' honkies." Beside him, Chiodo felt Hammond trembling. "Let's go, you can't stare these fucking animals down. Let's go."

20

Two teen-age girls minced out of the shadows on their side of the street, swinging hips and grinning. As they started to pass, one girl stopped on the dirt strip between the sidewalk and the street glaring at Chiodo. "*You* stand in the dirt, motherfucker," she said. "Don't you make *me* walk in the dirt. Didn't your momma teach you no manners, pig?" Chiodo grabbed her by the arm. "Let go of me. Let go, white scum!"

Hammond wrenched his hand off the girl. "Let her go, dammit. Are you crazy, man? Let her go."

"I'm going to lock her up for harassment."

"Like hell you are." Hammond waved the girl away. "Get out of here," he said. She hip-wiggled across the street, laughing to the crowd. "Hey, that motherfucker's gonna lock me up." She turned and screamed, "Hey, go home and lock up your momma!"

Hammond tugged at Chiodo's arm. "Let's get out of here."

"No. Let's call an assist and wipe out this corner."

"Dammit, you're out of your fucking mind, man. Let's go."

Sulking in his frustration, Chiodo retreated with his partner to the sound of hoots and jeers.

"Listen, kid," Hammond was saying, "it don't pay to be no hero on this job. Get your ass killed, for what? We lost a radio car on that corner last month. Molotov cocktails turned it into an inferno. How the guys got out alive I'll never know, but they did and not a scratch. They were damned lucky. Remember one thing, kid. This is a job. Like any other job, we all look forward to payday. The paycheck puts bread on the table, not the fucking medals. You've gotta be around to collect that paycheck."

Two blocks away, Chiodo saw the flashing lights of a radio car. People were moving in front of the lights. As they hurried toward the car, the voice of Sergeant Mack boomed through the night. "Get 'em both in the car. Both of them. See if you can stop that bleeding."

"What happened?" Hammond was wheezing for breath. Mack's driver, a big, heavy-handed man, was wrestling a handcuffed prisoner into the back of the patrol car. By the inside light, Chiodo saw another black man on the floor, blood oozing from his back.

"We were coming down the block to check on you guys when this fight started on the stoop over there," the driver said. "That guy there gets up and starts to run. This character here pulls a knife and sticks it right into his back."

"Who's gonna take the collar?" Sergeant Mack said.

"Sarge, I don't want no fucking collar," his driver said. "It's too late for night court, and I'm damned if I want to come in in the morning."

Mack turned to Hammond. "Why don't you take it, then?"

"I'd rather not, sarge."

"I'll take the collar, sarge."

The sergeant glanced at Chiodo and shook his head. "Rooks don't make collars in my outfit."

"Come on, sarge, let me take him."

"No. We'll find somebody who wants it."

They all climbed into the patrol car. As it sped toward the station house, light flashing, Mack radioed for an ambulance to stand by and made several calls to other units. No one wanted to take the arrest. The sergeant put the microphone into its cradle and looked at his driver. "You're it, Casey. You take the collar." Casey gave him a tight-lipped nod.

At the station, Chiodo helped type out the arrest forms and fingerprint cards on the knife assailant, saw him into a detention cell for the night and managed to drink a quick cup of coffee before he and Hammond returned to Post. They were let out of the cruiser at 11:45 P.M. with two hours and fifteen minutes of duty left. Ten minutes later, two uniformed TPF men from the adjoining post approached them on foot. "Psst. Hammond."

The TPF men had spotted three Negro males stripping a car on the other side of the block. "I'll take the collar," one of the TPF men said. "Okay by you?"

"Sure," Hammond said.

22

"Why don't you two go around the block that way and we'll go this other way. If they run, we've got 'em."

"Let's go, Chiodo."

This time, Chiodo was grateful for the darkness. They were almost upon the car thieves when Hammond stumbled on a patch of broken pavement. Confused in the darkness, the three ran straight toward the policemen.

Chiodo looped an arm around the throat of one man, but his aim was poor. The quarry slithered free and pounded down the street toward a patch of streetlight at the mouth of an alley. Chiodo ran after him, unsnapping his holster and shouting, "Halt! Halt or I'll shoot!" The .38 bucked, spitting flame at the sky. Instead of stopping the fugitive, the shots put wings to his feet. Chiodo stretched his legs into a loping sprint, the gun still aimed skyward. Suddenly, his foot snagged a chunk of broken curbing. Then he was pitching headlong into the street, hands outstretched. He crashed into the gutter in a grinding, grunting heap, and a bolt of pain smashed through his right hand. He lay there, gasping, as footfalls of his intended prisoner faded into the alley. Chiodo slowly pushed himself erect and dusted off his uniform. A gaping hole was gouged in the heel of his right hand, and the thumb was numb. Pain stabbed at his right hip, and his knees and elbows were skinned raw. As he limped back toward Hammond, the other two TPF men arrived herding two prisoners.

Chiodo's holster was empty. He turned back and found the pistol lying in the alley, its barrel marred by an ugly scratch. When he rejoined the others, they were all three wrestling with one of the prisoners. The man had slumped to the ground and locked his arms around a broken fence post.

"Let go, you bastard. Let go!"

"The son of a bitch don't want to let go."

Chiodo's wrath boiled up inside. "What's the matter?" he said.

"This prick doesn't want to be cuffed."

23

"Doesn't want to be cuffed!" With a growl, Chiodo leaped at the prisoner, slammed a foot into his ribs, grabbed a handful of hair, planted his foot on his spine and snapped the head backward. "All right, man!" came the gurgling cry. "All right! All right!" The hands released their grip on the post, and Hammond snapped on the cuffs.

"Hey, man," said one of the TPF men, "take it easy."

"Take it easy bullshit!" Chiodo shouted. "You're gonna take that shit from this—this—"

"You don't know this neighborhood." The TPF man glanced around nervously at the dark heads peering down from tenement windows and a crowd that had gathered silently nearby.

"Fuck this neighborhood," Chiodo said.

Moments later an unmarked Chevrolet pulled up, followed by a radio car. Two nondescript black men got out of the unmarked car. "Hey, what've you got here?" They wore goatees and Afro haircuts.

"Two for GLA."

"We're on our way to the house. Want us to take them?"

"Yeah. We'll follow along in the radio car."

Swiftly the men hustled the prisoners into the back of their car and drove away. Chiodo watched the vanishing taillights.

"What the hell was that?" he said.

"They're our guys. NNTF. Neighborhood Nighttime Task Force. They're TPF in plainclothes."

"Well, I'll be damned."

As they rode to the station in the radio car, Chiodo's thumb began to throb. But he kept thinking of the two plainclothesmen. They had been indistinguishable from the typical street idlers of the ghetto. The prospect of doing such police work intrigued him.

As Chiodo walked into the Precinct station house, Detective Dave Fraley looked up in surprise. "What the hell happened to you?"

Chiodo, his hand wrapped in a bloody cloth and his uniform torn and filthy, explained.

24

"Stubborn guinea bastard," said Fraley, "don't you listen to what anybody says? I told you not to get involved. What are you doing chasing people? If your partner wants to make a collar, watch him make it, but don't get involved. Not even two months on the job and you've got an injury on your record. If you can't use that hand anymore, do you know what happens? You're off the job, stupid!"

Sergeant Mack walked into the room, his face set. "What are you, some kind of a dumbbell, Chiodo? You're not supposed to get hurt. Now I've gotta go through twenty pounds of paper work."

"Gee, sarge, I'm—"

"Shut up. Just shut the fuck up."

"Take it easy on the kid, sarge," said Fraley. "He's got a pretty bad hand there. We should get him to a hospital."

Mack glowered. "I take care of my people," he hissed.

"Hey, sarge," said Chiodo, "do I get a collar?"

The sergeant turned, gritting his teeth. "Chiodo, you're in enough trouble already."

"Come on, sarge, I deserve the collar. I busted my fucking hand for it."

"Stop busting my balls, you ain't taking no collar." Mack shuffled away, muttering, "Probies! How come I always get stuck with winners?"

A radio car drove Chiodo to Brooklyn's Wyckoff Heights Hospital. In the emergency room Chiodo expected to find sympathy and quick treatment for a uniformed cop injured on duty. The receiving nurse gave him a glance of icy indifference. "Over there," she said, waving a pencil at a line of waiting civilians.

More than an hour passed before a foreign doctor gave the hand a cursory inspection, wrote out a slip and sent him to x-ray. Thirty minutes later another doctor came out of the film room and cleared his throat. "Nothing broken, but I think you tore some ligaments in the thumb." The doctor swabbed Merthiolate over the wound, wrapped the hand in an elastic bandage and filled out another form. A radio car carried Chiodo back to the station house, where the desk lieutenant frowned down from his lofty seat. "You the kid that got hurt? You've got to wait for the duty captain and make a report."

"The duty captain, lou?"

"Yeah, he'll be here in a while. Make yourself comfortable, kid."

It was 4:30 A.M. when the duty captain walked in carrying a clipboard and a ball-point pen.

"All right, what happened, kid? What's your story?"

The ball-point pen scratched briskly as Chiodo talked.

"Okay. You got a witness to this?"

"Yeah, my partner."

"Where is he?"

"He went off duty at two."

"Who's your boss, kid? Doesn't he know that every on-the-job injury's got to be confirmed by a witness?"

The hand beat a tattoo of pain. Chiodo wished his heart would stop pumping. "What if I didn't have a witness, captain? Does that mean the injury wouldn't count?"

"You'd still be injured, kid, but it might not be accepted as a job injury. That does make a difference."

"I'd fight that, captain."

"Sure, kid, fight City Hall. You've got a lot to learn, rook, so let me give you a piece of advice. Don't make waves." The ball-point pen slipped into the captain's pocket.

Dawn was breaking as Chiodo arrived home, stepped into the bedroom and touched the shoulder of his sleeping wife. Linda stirred and opened her eyes.

"Don't get excited," he began, "but I got hurt. Nothing serious. . . ."

Linda blinked, fully awake, and sat up in bed. "Oh, no!"

The hand would take three weeks to heal. Under departmental rules a man on injured status was not even allowed to leave his home without special permission. Suddenly, Chiodo was a captive in his own house.

When the pain left him, boredom settled in. Within three days he was pacing the floor. He went back to the police surgeon. "I'm going out of my mind, doc. Can't I go back to work?"

"No deal. Relax, kid. Enjoy it."

"Look, I'm supposed to have eight hours of class one day a week at the academy. That's day after tomorrow. Can I go?"

The surgeon shrugged and gave him a slip. Classwork was approved, but no gym. And he would have to wear civilian clothes. No uniform on sick leave.

At the academy the captain was up to his ears in paper work. "What do you need, kid?" Chiodo handed him the slip.

"I'm out on job injury, captain. Here's a note from the surgeon, says I can come back to the academy."

The captain was glum. "What the hell did you go and do that for, kid? Do you know how much paper work I've got to write up on you now?"

"I'm sorry to be so much trouble."

The captain read the note. "This is even worse. You can't even take your full eight hours, only four out of the eight. Your first four hours is supposed to be gym, but it says here you can't take gym. What am I supposed to do with you? Why didn't you just stay home?"

"Sorry, captain."

"Eager beavers." He sighed heavily. "Okay, listen, kid, can you keep your mouth shut?"

"Sure."

"Tell you what I'll do. I'll put you down for the full eight hours on paper, see. But instead of going to gym, you just get lost for a while this afternoon. Take in a movie or something from four to eight o'clock. I don't want to see you around here. Got that?"

"Right, captain."

A movie, then. That was fine. He loved movies. What was showing near the academy? *No Way To Treat a Lady.* Okay, he would see a movie.

He was in the balcony of the neighborhood theater, along with a handful of other patrons, all men. Halfway through the film, a man came and sat down beside him. Thin, sweet-smelling. Chiodo was annoyed. Empty seats all around and the guy had to plop down right next door. The man stirred in his seat. The backs of his fingertips brushed Chiodo's knee. An accident, no doubt. He ignored the touch. The fingers drew away. Then they came back. This time it was no accident. The touch lingered on his knee. Then the fingers moved, exploring.

"Knock it off," Chiodo muttered.

But the fingers remained. The man's breathing became audible. The fingers caressed his leg, moving higher. Chiodo's mind broke away from the movie. What the hell was he supposed to do now? Should he bust the guy, right there in the theater? No, that was no good. The captain would raise hell. The rookie was supposed to be in gym class, on paper at least. The captain would have to write out another report. The fingers moved on.

"Knock it off, I said. Go play someplace else."

Chiodo reached for his back pocket and quietly drew out the blackjack with his good hand. Okay, sport, don't say you weren't warned. Folding his arms, he tucked the blackjack under his left armpit and waited. The fingers reached his thigh. The man was trembling. Chiodo raised the blackjack then, and came down hard. Whack!

"Yeeeeeowwww!"

The scream crashed through the theater, and the man surged to his feet, cradling his hand. "Get your ass out of here, queer," Chiodo hissed. "I'm a cop." The sufferer needed no bidding. He raced up the steps and along the aisle, still screaming, and vanished down the stairs.

Chiodo's leg hurt where he had struck the hand so hard. With the screams still echoing in his mind, he tried to concentrate again on the movie. Footsteps came down toward his seat. Three men leaned over, giggling and posturing. "What happened, sweetie? Have a fight with your boy friend?"

"Beat it."

They scurried away. An hour went by.

He had forgotten the incident by the time the old man came. The old man carried a rolled umbrella and sat down beside him, giving off the same sweetish smell of perfume. This time there was no lingering touch of fingertips. The old man grabbed Chiodo's leg in a viselike grip.

"Hey! Scram, old man. I'm a cop." He flashed the shield under the old man's nose. "Get your queer ass out of here."

The hand drew away. "Well, pardon me!" The old man left.

The movie was spoiled. Hell, he couldn't stay here all evening fighting off queers.

Chiodo left the theater and walked the streets until it was time to go to class.

Two weeks later he was pleading with the police surgeon to let him go back to work. The surgeon eyed the thumb doubtfully. "You can't use a gun with that thumb." Chiodo convinced him that all police pistols were double-action weapons and it was unnecessary to cock the hammer. Grudgingly, the doctor gave in. "Hell, kid, if you want to work, go to work. I'll put you back."

In the fall he was back in the academy full time, dividing his days between classwork and gym. Classroom instructors put heavy stress on the penal code, search-and-seizure laws, civil rights, culpability and reasonable doubt.

"This is the new era of police work. Today, you don't beat in their heads. Remember, society is watching, and every man who goes out of this academy is expected to set an example. The days are past when you gave a man a badge and a gun and put him on the street to enforce the law as he saw it. Today, you're a psychologist, a sociologist, a marriage counselor, lawyer, doctor and more. A combination, in short, of many things. As for the law, you had better know it, because your decisions on the street, made in crisis, will be picked apart later by legal eagles who've got all the time in the world to second-guess your actions and are well paid for their trouble."

With these lectures ringing in their ears, the trainees would move to the gym for grueling afternoons of boxing, judo, elementary karate, running, rope climbing, and instruction in first aid, delivering babies and mouth-to-mouth resuscitation. "Now, we are aware that this will not always be enjoyable. It's one thing to apply mouth-to-mouth resuscitation to a sharp blonde with big tits, lying on the beach in her bikini, and another to give it to some Bowery skel who may puke in your mouth. We'll expect you to use your judgment."

In the gym, too, instructors often had a different view of survival in the street. Trainees were reminded that policemen were being shot, stomped, hacked, run over by cars and beaned with bricks. "Yeah, I know what they tell you in class," a barrel-chested instructor said to Chiodo's squad, "but I'm telling you something else. When you're out there, watch your ass. It's better to make a mistake and be alive in front of the grand jury than to get killed and let some punk be the one answering the questions." To Chiodo and others already seasoned by street duty, the words of the gym instructors were especially welcome.

As Christmas neared, the call again went out for extra men. This time, instead of a TPF assignment, Chiodo was sent to the 108th Precinct as a regular patrolman. "Okay, rook," said the sergeant, "you're going to watch stores."

It was dull, uneventful duty. Night after night, from four to midnight, Chiodo paced off his small beat in front of a line of gift shops, dime stores, department stores and card shops, jostled by shoppers and bombarded with questions. "Officer, where do I find kitchenware?" One evening, in a driving rain, he took shelter in a liquor store, drank a soda and watched the shoppers splashing past. A radio car cruised down the block, turned and cruised back. Chiodo hurried out. The car slid to the curb. "Chiodo," shouted the driver, "the sergeant's looking for you."

"What's up?"

30

"We've got a DOA in an apartment and he wants you to sit with it."

"Sit with a dead body?"

"Right."

As they rode through the rainy streets, Chiodo remembered an academy lecture. Whenever a person was found dead, an officer was required to remain with the body until a death certificate was signed by the medical examiner or a private physician.

The apartment was on the fifth floor of a posh building with crystal chandeliers and carpeted hallways. Chiodo walked into 5-D and found the sergeant writing out a report at the dining table. A woman sat grieving on the couch. In a chair near her sat an elderly man, his feet on a hassock and a cigarette in his hand. Another couple, who appeared to be neighbors, watched in somber silence. Chiodo looked around the room and glanced into the bedroom. He was puzzled. "Sergeant," he said, "where's the stiff?"

From the couch came a choked sob. The neighbor couple glared at him. The sergeant grimaced and pulled him aside.

"There, stupid, there's the stiff." He pointed to the man in the chair, holding the cigarette. Chiodo noticed then that the cigarette was out. "Did you expect to find a sign on his chest?" The sergeant stalked away, saying, "Don't leave until your relief shows."

Chiodo found a place to sit. The wall clock ticked loudly.

"That's the way we found him," the woman said finally, "sitting there in his favorite chair. It was his heart. He was seventy-two."

At eleven o'clock a relative arrived, shaking the rain from his umbrella. The man was a cousin from upstate. "Hi, Meg," he said casually, and walked over to the deceased. "Well, well, well, Fred looks great."

"Please don't touch the body," Chiodo said.

31

"Sure, officer. Don't he look great, though? What a way to go. Fred always did have style. . . ."

At 12:20 Chiodo's relief arrived. He was a regular precinct patrolman. Chiodo met him at the door. "Don't do what I did," he whispered. "The body is sitting over there in the chair."

The man grinned broadly. "Yeah, I know," he said.

"You know?"

"The whole damned precinct knows. 'Hey, where's the stiff?' Hah, hah, hah . . ."

Chiodo walked glumly out into the rain.

3

The Night Watch

Spring quickened the life of the city, with warm sunny days and kites coasting over Central Park. Across the vast reaches of Brooklyn, Queens and the Bronx, dogwood flowered and crocuses made yellow splotches in the yards. Manhattan's office girls shed their coats, to let skirts fly and enliven the lunch-hour scenery of Park Avenue, while above them the soaring glass façades of skyscrapers reflected blue sky and drifting clouds. In Harlem and Greenwich Village, laundry snapped from window clotheslines without freezing, and people could take walks wearing light sweaters in the evenings. Precinct lieutenants noted the usual spring rise in muggings.

"Chiodo, tomorrow night you're assigned to Six-six Precinct, Brooklyn."

"How come?"

"Sergeant's exams the next day. That means eighteen thousand guys get time off. It happens about once every three years. You rookies have to fill in, along with supervisors and a few old-timers who aren't taking the exams. But the Six-six is a quiet precinct. They'll probably put you on patrol with some hairbagger."

Because of the frequent interruptions for street duty, the academy course had been extended far beyond its normal length. Through the winter and into spring, the trainees had alternated between classrooms, the gym, the firing range and the streets. Now, ten days before graduation, he was again being pulled out for temporary assignment. Thirty minutes before the tour of duty was to begin, Chiodo walked into the Brooklyn station house.

His partner for the night of April 12, 1969, was Pete Slade, a heavy, baldish man with more than 20 years on the force. They would man Radio Motor Patrol 1156 over a broad range of sectors from 10:00 P.M. to 8:00 A.M., covering part of the evening shift and all of the midnight shift.

"Looks like we've got a busy night, kid." Slade stuffed a battered pipe with Prince Albert tobacco and popped a kitchen match into blaze with his thumbnail. "We're covering for a dozen cars."

Things began slowly, but picked up as the evening wore on. They checked out false burglar alarms, a domestic fight, which had ended by the time they arrived, two complaints of prowlers who were not to be found and a barking dog. By midnight the calls had slowed and they took their meal at a small diner. There was no check, so Chiodo left a dollar tip. Slade frowned. "Put that back in your pocket, kid. You want to spoil these people?" Chiodo ignored him and left the dollar.

At 2:00 A.M. the radio crackled. "Central to RMP eleven-fifty-six."

"Eleven-fifty-six. Kay."

"Report of a disturbance in the bar at Thirty-ninth and Eighth."

"Ten-five that address. Kay."

"Thirty-ninth and Eighth Avenue."

34

"Ten-four."

From outside the Happy Time Bar they heard the sounds of smashing furniture and breaking glass. "Stay in the car, kid. Don't want you rooks getting hurt." Slade ambled into the bar and Chiodo heard him bellow above the din. "All right, knock it off!" Surprisingly, the fighting stopped.

Chiodo walked in behind his partner. The place was wrecked. Broken tables and chairs littered the floor. A man sat holding his bleeding head and moaning. Two other customers were bleeding from head and face wounds. A leathery, gray-haired man came over to Slade.

"I'm a retired sergeant from the job," the gray-haired man said.

"Yeah?" Slade lit his pipe and motioned to the man on the floor. "Who did this guy in?"

"I did."

"What did you do that for?"

"The guy started on my son-in-law, so I laid him out."

Slade seemed to be grappling with a decision. "We've got to get this straightened out," he said. "I don't want to take you in, but we did get a call on it."

The bartender, a pale, paunchy little man behind a white apron, came from behind the bar with a wet towel. He handed the towel to a young woman, who pressed it to the head of the man on the floor. The bartender walked up to Slade and whispered, "Hey, can you guys put this outside?" Slade grunted.

As the injured man was being helped to his feet, the patrolman walked over to him and said, "You'll have to come with us to the station."

Chiodo, meanwhile, was questioning the gray-haired man.

"What did you hit him with?"

"Pool cue."

The injured man got into the back of the patrol car. The young woman opened the door of another car parked in front of the bar. A young child was in the front seat.

"How come we're taking this guy to the house?" Chiodo asked his partner.

"Shut up, kid."

At the station, Slade led the man into an office. A bandage had been wrapped around his head. Blood oozed through the white gauze.

"You don't want to press charges," said Slade.

"Yes I do. I want the old fart locked up."

"Naw, you don't want to press charges. You've gotta live in this neighborhood, you know. There's no need to make things worse than they are already."

"I want him locked up."

"Tell me the story," Slade said.

The injured man, Peter Black, and his wife Louise had been to a party. On the way home, accompanied by their 18-month-old son, they had decided to stop at the Happy Time for a drink. As they drank, the retired sergeant and his son-in-law arrived. The son-in-law demanded to know whose car was parked outside. "There's a baby in that car. That baby ought to be home in bed." The fight started. Black knocked down the son-in-law. The old sergeant jumped in with the pool cue. Louise leaped onto the old sergeant's back. Several of Black's friends joined the melee. The sergeant started smacking heads with the pool cue.

Slade finally persuaded Peter Black not to press charges, and the man was taken to a hospital to have his head stitched. Then Chiodo and Slade drove back to the bar. "Stay in the car, kid," said Slade. He went inside to talk with the bartender. Ten minutes later he was back. RMP 1156 resumed its patrol.

"It's all right, kid," Slade said. "Just write in your memo book that the fight occurred at Thirty-ninth Street and Eighth Avenue, approximately a hundred feet from the bar."

"No," Chiodo said. "It was inside the bar, and that's how I'm writing it."

"Look, kid, don't give me no shit. Now, you're on probation, and I know you don't want to make a lot of waves. I'm telling

36

you the fight was outside the bar, and nobody's gonna think any different."

"If that bar owner is afraid of losing his license, that's his worry, not mine," Chiodo said.

The debate went on until finally Chiodo agreed merely to put the address in his memo book, without indicating whether the fight was inside or outside the building.

Slade seemed satisfied. "Okay, and how about giving me your name and phone number, kid. I'll want to get together with you later on. This thing's worth about a deuce. It's really not taking, you understand. No graft or anything like that. This happens every day. The guy is grateful and wants to do a little something in return. We'll just split it, a hundred apiece."

"No, thanks."

"Look, kid, I know what you're thinking, and it isn't like that at all. We just don't get paid enough on this job, know what I mean? What the hell, every day you're out here risking your ass, and for what? Nobody appreciates a cop, nobody but your own neighborhood people. You got to take care of them, the businessmen. Then you're happy, they're happy, everybody's happy and gets along. So what I'll do, see, is send you half when this guy comes across. That's fair, you're my partner."

Chiodo was uncomfortable. He did not wish to continue the conversation. He told Slade he would jot down his home telephone number and probably get in touch with him sometime. But even as he wrote the number on the back of his memo pad, Chiodo knew he would not make the call.

The radio sent them to a clothing store, where another faulty burglar alarm was ringing. They notified the owner. At a coin laundry the lights of the cruising patrol car illuminated a broken window. As they stopped, a neighbor woman came out in her robe and told them that two people had tried to force the front door of the laundry but fled when she turned on her outside light. The attempted break-in was reported. The patrol resumed.

"Central to RMP eleven-fifty-six. Prowler in an apartment building, five-one-eight-two Eighth Avenue. . . ."

A young woman sat on the third-floor steps of the building, shouting and crying. People in robes and pajamas clustered around the landing, watching her. "Lousy bastards!" she shouted. "Lousy bastards, all of you . . ." Her frosted blonde wig was twisted, and mascara streaked her face. "Fuck the whole damned world!"

The building's occupants said that apparently she had wandered in off the street. "Drunken broad. Officer, it's five o'clock in the morning."

They escorted her to the patrol car and asked where she lived. The woman stammered out an address six blocks away. It was a brick apartment building. They let her out of the car there. Half an hour later they, were summoned back by irate neighbors. "She don't live here, officer. She's drunk. She woke up the whole building, pounding on doors."

"Okay, lady. We don't want to take you in. Now where do you live?"

"Drop dead, fat-ass," she said. "I don't wanna go home."

"Come on, sweetheart, don't give me none of your shit," said Slade. "Where do you live?"

"Okay. Okay." She gave him a second address, a tenement at Ninth Avenue and Forty-third Street. "Sorry," she said, belching. "Won't do it again." They watched her totter into the building.

Twenty minutes later RMP 1156 sat parked on a side street. Chiodo and Slade, their radio quiet at last, relaxed and watched the morning unfold over a sleeping neighborhood.

"Central to eleven-fifty-six."

"Eleven-fifty-six. Kay."

"Report of prowler at four-three-one-oh Ninth Avenue."

"Eleven-fifty-six, ten-four."

"Shit," said Slade, "it's that broad again."

"Maybe not this time."

"We ain't going back there."

"Let's go back. It might be a real prowler call."

"Naw, kid, I say it's that drunken broad again. I'm tired of hauling her ass all over town. If we go back again you're gonna have to lock her up. Is that what you want?"

"No, but let's go see who's right?"

It was the same scene, but this time she seemed even drunker and more disheveled than before. While angry neighbors glared, Slade marched up the steps. She screamed abuse at him. By now the wig was gone entirely. "Shut up," fumed Slade. "Get outta here. You've had us running around all night. You oughta go home, bitch."

"Pig!" she shrieked. "Everybody's against me. I hate this fucking world and everybody in it!" She lurched to her feet and slapped Slade in the face. He slapped her back.

"Hey!" Chiodo shouted. He led her down the stairs. "Tell me where you live," he said. "You don't want to . . ."

She staggered out to the patrol car, opened the back door and crawled inside. More tears flowed. "All you guys wanna do is screw me," she wailed. "That's all anybody wants." She pulled up her skirt. "Go ahead, then. Screw me."

"We'd better lock her up, kid," Slade said. "If she starts this shit, we're both in a jam. I'm calling the house."

"Fuck you," she said. "Lock me up."

"Eleven-fifty-six to Central." Slade's voice was tired.

"Go ahead, eleven-fifty-six."

"Transporting one white female to the house from four-three-one-oh Ninth Avenue. Public intox. Kay."

"Ten-four, eleven-fifty-six."

There were no policewomen at the station to search the prisoner. As they waited for the wagon to take her to another precinct, she began to sober up. "Oh, I shouldn't have gotten smashed," she said. "It's my boy friend. We had a fight. The only reason he goes with me is to have a piece of ass on the side. He's married and is gonna stay married." She blew her nose into a tissue.

"Have you got a job?" Chiodo asked.

39

"I'm a cocktail waitress."

At 9:00 A.M. a paddy wagon arrived, and Chiodo followed it in his car to the 78th Precinct. There, a policewoman made the search, and forty-five minutes later they were waiting for the court arraignment. The case was not called until 11:40. She was released on a $50 cash bond. Chiodo signed out at 11:50, nearly 14 hours after he had gone on duty.

"Crazy chick," he muttered.

He put the car into gear and headed for Queens.

Ten days later, on April 22, 1969, Chiodo graduated from the academy and pinned on the silver collar insignia of the TPF. Normally graduation would have called for a celebration, but their training had been so prolonged that the ceremony was merely an anticlimax.

A few days later Chiodo and Linda visited his parents' house. His father was not in a happy mood.

"So you're a full-fledged *sbirro* now. *Marrone.*"

"I'm going to make a novena," his mother said.

"What for?" said Linda.

"Maybe he will get fired."

The TPF was now 1000 strong, the pick of the police department. Deputy Chief Inspector Charles McCarthy vowed that his men could mobilize against disorder in any borough within 30 minutes. Quiet, resourceful and energetic, the TPF commander had started his own career 23 years before, pounding a beat in Queens. "A fixed number of policemen assigned to a fixed piece of real estate is necessary and desirable," he said, "but crime is not static. Police should also be able to move immediately to where crime is happening."

In the decade since they were first formed in 1959, the tactical squads had grown from a nucleus of 75 men. But for all the glamour surrounding the force, Chiodo knew from experience that day-to-day patrols could be dull. He was more intrigued by the newly formed decoy units of policemen who went into the streets dressed as hippies, doormen, working women, bus drivers, garbage collectors, businessmen, cab drivers and news vendors. The decoys were scattered through the city as bait for muggers, thieves, rapists and cutthroats. Each decoy teamed with at least two backup partners. The special units had been formed in response to a rash of assaults and muggings in the Hassidic community of Brooklyn. Hebrew-speaking TPF men posed as orthodox Jews in beaver hats, caftans and theatrical beards applied by makeup men. They quickly nabbed 15 muggers.

So successful was the ruse that decoys moved into the garment district against a wide range of crimes, from gambling to thievery, stickups and truck hijacking. Posing as idlers, buyers and workmen pushing hand trucks, they made 1200 arrests. Others masqueraded as women to thwart mashers in Central Park, and decoys went after gangs of young thieves who preyed upon the cars of theatergoers in Times Square. "Crime is a hydra-headed monster," McCarthy said. "Cut off one head and another shoots out and starts biting." It was the TPF's job to be ready for the next bite.

In his temporary duty at various precincts, Chiodo had seen some of the decoys at the station houses. Usually they were ragged, unshaven men who wandered in and out and kept to themselves. Two TPF patrolmen with whom he had worked in uniform, Tom Blake and Pat Mayhew, were now assigned to decoy teams in Brooklyn. When Chiodo learned that he would be assigned to a Brooklyn uniformed squad, he began plotting his next move.

The 71st Precinct station house was headquarters for the Brooklyn decoys. They had their own muster room where the men gathered for evening roll call. Chiodo's primary duty assignment for three months was the Crown Heights section, a relatively peaceful area where excitement usually meant an argument with a Jewish merchant over a parking ticket.

The peace of Crown Heights, of course, could be deceptive.

Two uniformed precinct patrolmen were ambushed by a crazed young black militant as they entered an apartment house to investigate a family dispute. Both men were cut down by shotgun blasts from behind a bush. The assailant fled, eluding a citywide manhunt, and neither patrolman ever fully recovered from his wounds.

Police undercover men infiltrating Black Panther cells in Brooklyn were coming up with frequent plots to assassinate policemen. Uniformed men were constantly on edge. Chiodo and his partners walked their posts warily, keeping close to buildings and eyeing rooftops and slow-moving cars. While the 71st Precinct itself, covering a large area south of Eastern Parkway, was made up largely of nonviolent Jewish and black West Indian families, the danger came from militants and hoodlums drifting in from adjoining black neighborhoods.

Shortly after two o'clock one morning as Chiodo and his partner checked out from their tour of duty, a rooftop sniper with a high-powered rifle opened up on a cruising patrol car, riddling the vehicle with bullets. Miraculously neither of the two patrolmen in the car was hit by the gunfire, although both were cut by flying glass. As emergency squads blanketed the neighborhood, Chiodo joined the hunt for the sniper. He was not found. When the search was called off two hours later, Chiodo gave his partner, Bill Parini, a bleak smile. "In case you don't remember, old buddy, we were standing on that corner two hours before this happened, waiting for the sergeant to come by and make the scratch."

After that, they no longer stood still in the open, even when it was time for the sergeant to make his rounds and sign their memo books. If you had to be a target, it was better to be a moving one.

Chiodo got into the habit of arriving early at the station house each day. The decoy men passed through the uniformed sitting room, going to and from roll call. He soon reestablished his acquaintance with Blake and Mayhew.

"Hey, kid, how're you doing?"

"Fine, Tommy. How's the decoy work?"

"Great."

"What's it really like?"

"Man, we've got it all over you uniform guys. I'd hate to be back in the bag, believe me. This decoy stuff is a ball."

Blake was an aggressive, solid little Irishman with four years in TPF. Just five feet eight inches tall, he had barely made the height requirements. His baby face masked a lightning temper. At 25 Tom Blake was a woman-chasing bachelor who also loved a brawl. Pat Mayhew, by contrast, was a quiet, even-tempered man, slow to anger and conservative in his habits. Two years older than Blake, he preferred to subdue an unruly subject with reason, if possible, but also had a reputation for aggressive police work and nerve. Together, they were a well-balanced team that made numerous arrests. Permanence in decoy work required high numbers on the monthly performance sheets. The job also demanded certain special qualities.

"It's a little different, working decoy," Blake said. "The uniform has its psychological effects. But when you're in raggedy old clothes, that's something else again. When you move on a guy, you've got to move hard. Keep the scumbag backing up all the time. A lot of street punks pretend they don't know you're a cop, even after you've flashed the shield."

"I'd like working with you guys," Chiodo said. "I'd like to get into decoy."

"Give it time, kid. You need a couple of years uniform experience first and a recommendation from your sergeant. Keep making collars and you'll get there. That's what they look for, a lot of numbers."

"Do they use fill-in men? When a regular man doesn't make it—say, he's had to go to court that day or something—how do they get a replacement?"

"That's done by the roll-call man in TPF headquarters. He keeps a list. There's a real nice guy down there named Ben Petrelli. You might talk to him some time."

If the game was numbers, Chiodo was not making an impressive score. Arrests on the Crown Heights post were few and far between. When one big opportunity to boost his stock did come, the episode bordered on the bizarre.

"You want numbers, kid?" a veteran told him. "Wait'll you work with Gimbel and his Gooneybirds. Those guys are fanatics on numbers. They've got a guy in that squad called The Wind. Little guy, blond, bundle of nerves, strange pale eyes. Patrolman Windom. He's Sergeant Gimbel's pet, the craziest son of a bitch that ever put on a uniform."

One day orders came down. The Third Squad and Gimbel's Gooneybirds would team up for a TPF crackdown on the drug-addict-infested 91st Precinct. Gimbel's 30 men had already been in the precinct two weeks and were hauling in more junkies than they could handle. Base for the operation was the station house of the neighboring 90th Precinct. Chiodo arrived there, glanced at the roster sheet and grimaced. His partner for the night: Patrolman Windom.

"How ya' doin? How ya' doin? I'm The Wind. Chiodo, ain't you? I'll call you Chi. We got Post Three, man. Gonna grab a lotta junkies, lotta numbers. Great. Great. Great."

The veteran's description, if anything, had fallen short. The Wind had a sharp, ratlike face and penetrating eyes, formed as if from two chunks of pale blue glass. His mouth was thin and cruel. His words came in a rush, tumbling over one another. His feet shuffled as he talked. The man reminded Chiodo of a sputtering powder keg. "They never arrest nobody in the Nine-one Precinct. Commander don't like paper work. He went on vacation and his executive officer called in the TPF. Hah, hah. Stone-junkie precinct, man. Stone junkies . . ."

As they rode out in Chiodo's car The Wind kept up his running chatter, eyes darting over the streets. Chiodo learned that in two years in the TPF the man had made a phenomenal 120 arrests. "Man, we got the best post there is. Hey, man, lotta collars."

44

Five blocks from the post they were met by two uniformed men from the adjoining Post Four, consisting of another of Gimbel's Gooneybirds, a patrolman named Scotty, and a man from Chiodo's squad. The other team parked their car behind Chiodo's. There was a quick conference between The Wind and Scotty. "We're gonna go in there and take a buncha them," The Wind said. "We'll just take the whole bunch. Let's go. Let's go." Then they were running down the sidewalk behind The Wind, holsters flapping.

"Hey," shouted Chiodo, "what's going on?"

"Come on, come on. Let's go!"

They were breathing hard as The Wind came to a stop in front of a tenement building. The eyes squinted toward the roof. "Up on the roof. Up on the roof," he shouted. "This is the time they shoot up, on the roof. Let's go!" They pounded up five flights of stairs. The Wind burst through a door and swept out onto the roof. A young Puerto Rican sat on the parapet. "Where's the shit, man?" screamed The Wind. "Where's the stuff?"

"Man, I ain't got nothin'."

"You're a fucking junkie. Look at them arms." The Wind grabbed the youth by the throat. "Where's the shit, man. Give!"

"Hey, take it easy," Chiodo said.

"Don't tell me to take it easy. I know how to handle junkies. Take it easy, huh?" The Wind threw the youth against a brick wall and frisked him. Nothing. "Search the roof. The stuff's hidden. They got it hidden somewhere." They searched and still found nothing. The Wind spotted a bottle of water on top of the stairwell. "Hah! There's the water. Ain't that water?"

The Puerto Rican shrugged.

"See? See? It's their fucking water. I'll fix 'em." He unzipped his trousers and urinated into the bottle. "There, that'll take care of their water. Quick. Down to the basement. Down to the basement." They clattered back down the stairs. The basement, too, was empty.

As Chiodo and the other man from his squad exchanged worried glances, The Wind conferred feverishly with Scotty. "You know that other place on Third Street? Know the place? Me and this kid—" he jerked his thumb at Chiodo "—we'll go in the alley. You and your partner bust in the door. Apartment Two-B, we got four in there last week, right? When they come piling out the window, we'll take 'em."

They ran down more streets. From windows and stoops people watched them, laughing. Windom was known. "Hey, Weend," somebody called, "you catch them, amigo." Windom and Chiodo dashed into an alley while Scotty and the other patrolman went through the front door. They waited, panting for breath. Then an upstairs window opened and two youths scrambled out onto the fire escape, spilling needles and glassine packets of heroin into the alley. The Wind drew his pistol. "You come down. You come down real slow, junkies, or I'll blow your fucking brains out." Then he was punching and slapping them, snapping on the handcuffs. Scotty's head emerged from the upstairs window. "Anybody else up there?" The Wind shouted. Scotty shook his head. "Okay, we'll meet you in front."

A rock sailed over them and caromed off a garbage can. Then came a tomato, just missing Chiodo and splattering on the wall of a building. Massed at the mouth of the alley were angry Puerto Ricans, shouting in Spanish. From the crowd came a shower of sticks, stones, bottles, eggs, tomatoes and chunks of brick. Windom grabbed a garbage-can lid as a shield and charged, Chiodo following him with the prisoners. "Get the fuck outta our way!" screamed The Wind. "I'll kill youse all, spic bastards!" The crowd made way just as a TPF car arrived. The Wind herded the prisoners into the car. "Take these guys. Take 'em," he shouted to Scotty. "We'll get more. Gotta get more." Then they were hurrying down the street again, leaving the crowd behind. Chiodo, dazed, followed The Wind around the corner.

Windom slowed his pace, eyes narrowing. "See those two guys coming toward us?" he said. Chiodo saw two young men, one small and thin, the other muscular, bullnecked and walking with the lumbering gait of a weight lifter. The giant stood a head taller than Chiodo himself. "The little guy's a junkie. I chased him last week. Stand here and we'll get 'em when they come by."

As the two started to pass, Windom reached out and grabbed the small man by the shoulder. "Remember me? Remember me? You got away from me last week. I gotcha today!"

"Hey, man, leave him alone." The big man's voice rumbled like a diesel truck.

"You're under arrest, both of you!"

A huge hand grabbed The Wind by the collar, lifted him off the sidewalk and threw him down. As Chiodo's partner went sprawling, the small man sprinted away. With a lunge, Chiodo was on the giant's back. He was shaken off like a terrier. The Wind bounced to his feet and both of them grappled with the mass of muscle and flesh. Chiodo grasped his nightstick bayonet-style, as he had been taught in the academy. The point of the stick plunged into the massive midsection. "Ugh!" the giant grunted. Two meaty hands folded over the stick and pulled. Chiodo let his body go with the stick, hoping that the wrist thong would not break. The Wind scrambled onto the big man's back, pummeling with his fists. A crowd gathered, shouting for the giant. Tires squealed in the street and two more TPF men rolled out of a radio car. The four of them wrestled the giant down and handcuffed him behind his back.

"Get him in the car. In the car!" The Wind hurled punches at the handcuffed man. "I'm gonna beat this fucking guy. I'm gonna beat his head in." Kicks and blows rained on the giant as Chiodo tried to search him for weapons in the back seat of the car. The Wind was still screaming as they wrestled the big guy into the 90th Precinct station. They brought him to the lieutenant's desk, and something fell out of his trousers and clattered to the floor. Chiodo looked down in astonishment at a .22 pistol. "This cat is packing a Saturday-night special," someone said.

Windom burst into new paroxysms of fury. The mouth

twisted and the eyes flashed. "You had a gun! You had a gun!" He danced around the prisoner, spittle spraying from his mouth. "YOU HAD A GUN!" Windom seized the giant by the throat and shook him.

"Officer," shouted the lieutenant, "let go of that man!"

"He had a gun! A gun! A fucking gun!"

A clerk grabbed Windom and dragged him away, twisting and shouting. The lieutenant ordered Chiodo to take the prisoner into another room. As they walked he felt dwarfed by the size of the man—and soon found out why; the prisoner was six feet four inches tall and weighed 250 pounds. He had spent five years in prison for selling narcotics.

"How'd you like it upstate?" Chiodo asked wryly.

"It was okay, man."

"What did you do for five years?"

"I lifted weights. Just lifted weights, man. Wanna know why?"

"Why?"

"So when I got out you fuckers couldn't push me around."

When Chiodo returned to the front office, Windom was calmer and Sergeant Gimbel was there, talking quietly to his favorite patrolman. Chiodo overheard him. "Good job, Wind. Hadda gun, huh? Good collar. Real good collar."

They hurried through the typing of arrest cards. Windom's excitement was rising again. "Gotta get back on the street, man. Get more. Get more." By the time they left the station he was almost dancing with anticipation. Back at the post The Wind fairly skipped along the street. He seemed to know everyone. "Hey, Felix, you got somethin' good for me? Get me some shit, man. Give me somebody."

"Hey, Wind, how are ya?"

Three boys came out of an apartment house. Blood dripped from one youth's arm. Windom pounced. "You just shot up, didn't you? Just shot up. Get back in that hallway, all of you. Back inside." The boys obeyed. "Where is it? Where's the shit?

48

Come on!" He frisked them, then ran his hands over the molding of the doorway, the radiator, the mailboxes. "Where's the shit?" He grabbed a boy and started slapping and cuffing.

"All right, Windom, knock off that crap," growled Chiodo.

"The kid's got it!" The pale eyes glittered. "They've got a stash here someplace, I tell you. They just shot up!"

Sergeant Gimbel pulled up outside in a radio car. "What've you got, Wind?" he called.

"These guys just shot up, sarge. I'm gonna take 'em."

"Take 'em for what?" Chiodo said. "We didn't find nothing."

"Yeah, I know," The Wind said, "but . . ."

"Sergeant, sergeant," shouted one of the Puerto Ricans. "Thees man here, he done illegal seech and serzure!"

"Shut up, you dumb spic," The Wind snapped. "It's search and seizure. How about that, sarge? We got a Puerto Rican junkie lawyer here."

"Better let 'em go, Wind," the sergeant said.

After a brief argument, Windom released the youths and stalked down the street muttering, "Gotta get more. We gotta get more."

"No, man," said Chiodo. "It's ten o'clock. There's a fire station down the block. I'm going to the firehouse. You can run around these streets like a nut by yourself. But frankly, pal, I think you'd better go see a headshrinker."

Chiodo walked away and did not see his partner again that evening. But even without him, The Wind made three more arrests. Chiodo had a feeling of foreboding about the man.

The experience left him restless and discontented. Back on duty in the Crown Heights section, he found himself with little to do. One afternoon he walked into a haberdashery shop to inform the merchant that the parking meter had expired on his car.

"You must be kidding, officer," came the reply. "It's already six thirty-five, and after seven you don't have to put money in the meter."

"Yeah, I know, but it's not seven yet," Chiodo said. "Put a dime in the meter."

"Look, we got you TPF guys in here to protect us from the blacks, not to bother law-abiding citizens. You know how much taxes I pay? I'm paying your salary in taxes."

"Look, just put a dime in the—"

"What's the matter, is your sergeant bothering you, officer?"

"Nobody's bothering me but you, mister. Either put a dime in the meter or I'm hanging a summons on your car."

At home Chiodo was out of sorts. "I feel like a night watchman," he told Linda. "There's got to be something better than this. Walk so many blocks this way and so many blocks that way, check in and check out, keep the memo book up to date, take your meal at nine, don't make waves."

"Give it time," she said. "You've just started."

"Yeah, but I'm beginning to wonder, babe, if I made a mistake. I want to be a cop, not a guard for a Jewish temple."

On one of his days off, in civilian clothes, he walked into TPF headquarters and introduced himself to Ben Petrelli.

"Hi, Chiodo. What can I do for you?"

"How do you get into a decoy unit?"

Petrelli was a meaty, calm man with a fierce pride in the TPF. A thousand men constantly shifted over the city's network of precincts, all with varying days off, vacations, sick leaves and absences for court appearances. His job was to keep track of them. In the process Petrelli also kept daily rosters of more than 100 decoys whose work schedules seemed to make little sense at all. But he was a patient, methodical man. As a sideline, he dabbled as a stockbroker.

"You're new to TPF, aren't you, Chiodo?"

"Two and a half months."

"Wait'll you get some more experience, then ask your sergeant to recommend you. That's my advice."

"But what's the basis for selecting men for decoy work?"

"They're volunteers, for starters. Some men like that kind of

50

thing, some don't. There's a lot of freedom, but it's rough. They need to be aggressive and well motivated. The big thing in decoy is numbers. Those with the highest monthly arrest totals stay on permanent assignment; the others go back into uniform. That's the way it works."

Petrelli had been anything but encouraging, but Chiodo sensed that he had made an impression. He walked out of the office with a strong feeling of optimism. From what the roll-call man had said, still another element carried weight in the picking of decoy men. Persistence.

Within a week he had called Petrelli twice requesting temporary assignment as a fill-in man.

"We've never put on an inexperienced man. Didn't I tell you that?"

"Well, there's no harm in trying," Chiodo said.

Petrelli chuckled and hung up.

It was a Friday night and the Jewish sabbath had begun. In the synagogues of Brooklyn the orthodox were coming out of services. Chiodo and a partner, Don O'Malley, were on radio motor patrol. A bearded man and his wife flagged them down.

"Officers, I've got a problem. My wife and I are locked out of our apartment."

"Where do you live?"

They lived three blocks away. At services he had discovered that the key was not in his pocket.

"Why don't you call a locksmith?"

"It is the sabbath. We cannot use the telephone."

"Okay, get in the car. We'll drive you."

"We cannot ride in a car."

"All right, then, we'll meet you there."

The couple trudged into the apartment building and stood with O'Malley and Chiodo at the elevator. Two minutes passed. Three.

"Officer, if you don't push the button the elevator will not come down."

"What's the matter, is your finger broken?"

"It is the sabbath, and—"

"Okay, okay."

The elevator came down. "We will walk up the stairs and meet you on the third floor," the bearded man said.

The door of the third-floor apartment bristled with locks. O'Malley shook his head. "You did a fine job of burglarproofing the place. It can't even be jimmied open. There's nothing we can do."

"Then break the door down."

"We can't break the door down. We're not authorized to break the door down."

"It is my apartment, and I am requesting that you break the door down."

"Sorry."

"If you don't, you are going to be in a lot of trouble. I know Mayor Lindsay and Inspector Horowitz."

"Good. Call Mayor Lindsay and get him to break your door down."

"Look, folks," said Chiodo, "I'd suggest you ask the building superintendent to do something, or maybe sleep in the hallway, anything. But we can't break down the door."

O'Malley and Chiodo started to walk away.

"One moment, officers. I want your names and your badge numbers. Write them down on a piece of paper."

"It's a shield number," O'Malley said. "Firemen have badges, cops have shields."

"Very well, then write down your shield numbers."

O'Malley tore a sheet from his memo pad and handed it to the man, along with a stub of pencil. "You write it," he said. The man refused to touch the paper.

"I can't write it," he said. "It is the sabbath."

"Then remember," O'Malley said. "O'Malley, two-one-three-four-seven. Chiodo, two-seven-nine-nine-six."

They walked out.

The next day Chiodo put in another call to TPF headquarters. "This is Patrolman Chiodo, Third Squad. Do you need a fill-in man for decoy?"

"Chiodo, how many times do I have to tell you . . ."

One evening the squad-room roster in the 71st Precinct station bore a curious entry, penciled at the bottom of the page. "RMP 6969. Betty the Bare, operator; Dee the Lip, recorder. Meal: anybody."

"What the hell does that mean?" Chiodo asked his partner for the evening, Joe Podrowski.

"Aw, that's Jerry Vandriesen's chicks. They ride around in a little blue Rambler. Real cop buffs. Somehow they know where all the posts are in the Seven-one. They come around, ask what time's your meal and take you for a ride. Pipe-job specialists."

"Man, I can't believe that. No chick would do that, ride around looking for cops to pick up."

"Hey, Chi, I know you're new around here, but don't bullshit me, you ain't that new."

"Yeah, but—"

"What time's our meal tonight? Nine o'clock? Okay, we're working Post Five, and Jerry—let's see—he and his partner have got Post Eight. Fine. We'll have our meal with them at a little pizza place I know. You'll see."

Jerry Vandriesen was a blondish, blue-eyed bachelor with a fondness for tailored uniforms and spit-shined shoes. As they waited for pizzas, Podrowski steered the conversation. "Jerry, tell Chiodo here about your sexcapades."

"Man, the greatest. Some broad on my post invited me up last night and she was a dog. I threw her on the bed and couldn't stand to look in her face, it was that bad. Turn you to stone. But I banged her anyhow. You guys can say what you want to, the best piece is an ugly bitch. Once in a while I land a beauty. But if I screwed only beauties I'd have gotten laid eight hundred times less last year. . . ."

The front door opened and two women came in. "Oooh, there he is," cooed one, a fat, washed-out blonde. "Oh, Jer-reeee."

"Well, if it ain't Betty the Bare and Dee the Lip!"

Both women were heavyset, with deep eye shadow and jingling bracelets. They fluttered over Vandriesen like huge birds, ruffling his hair, patting his cheek. "Jerry, you wanna take a ride?"

Vandriesen grinned at his partner. "What about it, Ed? You need to get fixed up?"

"Why not?" said Ed. The partners left their pizzas half-eaten and rode away in the blue Rambler.

Podrowski laughed. "Jerry says he ain't never kissed Betty the Bare. Twenty times, and he never kissed her. When he does kiss her, Betty says she'll buy him a steak dinner at Twenty-one."

Two days later, as Chiodo prepared to put on his uniform for work, the phone rang at his house in Queens.

"Patrolman Chiodo? This is TPF headquarters. Report to Two-four precinct tonight for decoy duty."

"Wh-what did you say?"

"We've got you down for fill-in tonight, decoy. Report to—"

"Yeah, yeah, I got that. The Two-four. But what do I wear?"

"Hell, wear old clothes."

He hung up the receiver, stared at it dazedly for a moment and then took a deep, deep breath.

"Yaaah-hoooo!"

4

Blindman's Buff

The 24th was a tough precinct on the fringes of Harlem. Stomach fluttering, Chiodo walked into the old station house wearing a faded, unpressed Army fatigue jacket, dungarees badly worn at the knees and a pair of dirty sneakers. The heavy service revolver felt bulky on his hip beneath the loosely hanging jacket. The desk lieutenant glared down at him from his high perch. In the corner, a uniformed cop got up from his chair. "Help you, mister?"

"Uh, I'm Patrolman Chiodo, TPF. I'm assigned to decoy tonight."

"Let's see your shield."

Chiodo fished the shield from his pants pocket. The officer inspected it and grunted. "I can't tell you damn decoy guys from the rest of the skels."

"Where's the decoy room?"

"Through that door, upstairs."

A huge black man stood at the lieutenant's desk, eyeing Chiodo. The man wore a bushy Afro, a dashiki, and horn beads strung around his neck. He smiled, displaying a mouthful of big teeth. "Um, looks like a bad-ass comin' to the Two-four," the black man said. Chiodo frowned and walked away.

The upstairs TPF room was a bleak, dusty place that smelled of sweat, stale tobacco smoke and moldy woodwork. Notices hung helter-skelter on a bulletin board that must have dated back to the Civil War. Desks and chairs were museum pieces. Men idled about the room dressed as street bums and toughs. In a corner a makeup man applied spirit gum to a set of false mustaches and affixed them to the upper lip of a lean, black-bearded man. On the opposite side of the room sat a shapely blonde in a black dress. The blonde smoked a cigarette and slouched in the chair, legs apart. Chiodo, ignored, wandered to the bulletin board, smoked a cigarette, listened to the murmur of talk. Then, bored, he studied the blonde.

A long-haired man in hippie clothes detached himself from a desktop and came over to Chiodo. "You dig the chick?" he said mildly.

"Not bad," Chiodo said.

"You must be new here."

"Uh-huh. I'm from Third Squad."

"Maybe I can fix you up with the chick."

"What is she, a policewoman?"

"Sort of."

"I've seen better faces, but the body ain't bad."

"Hey, George," said the hippie. "Kid here digs the chick."

"Yeah?" George, a paunchy, middle-aged man in a business suit and spectacles, joined them. "What's your name, kid?"

"Chiodo."

George grinned. Then he called across the room to the blonde. "Hey, Louie. Chiodo here really digs you. Says he'd like to get a little of that later. You wanna date tonight, Louie?"

The room erupted in laughter. Chiodo looked around at the odd assortment of faces leering at him. "Man, you got a real eye for broads," someone shouted.

56

The blonde scowled and jammed the cigarette into an ash-tray. "Why don't you bastards shut the fuck up!" roared the deep voice of Patrolman Louie Millard.

The blonde was a man!

Red-faced, Chiodo headed for the water cooler. As he drank, another decoy man came over and clapped him on the shoulder. "It's okay, kid, a lotta guys make the same mistake. Some of them wind up in a cell. Louie might look sexy in that getup, but he's tough as a sledgehammer. The sergeant picked him for skirts because he's small. He works Central Park, baiting mashers."

Sergeant Ed Maraney walked in with his clipboard. A dark man with a dent in his nose, Maraney shouted for quiet. As he did so, the big black man from downstairs entered the room and stood near Chiodo. In months to come Chiodo would often hear of the exploits of Ralph Brown, a decoy man who prowled the toughest, seamiest streets of the ghetto.

"The arrests have been good so far this month," Maraney began, "but we know that every scumbag in this neighborhood has got a gun, and you guys haven't been making gun collars—"

Brown gave a throaty laugh. "Sarge," he shouted, "I been meaning to talk to you about that. I got an idea to get me a gun collar. Maybe more than one."

"What's that, Brown?"

"But I've got to work it alone."

"Let's hear it."

"Well, I goes into one of them uptown soul bars, see. I'm cryin' and carryin' on something terrible. 'Them white mother-fucking pigs, they shot my boy. They killed my boy! Who's got a gun? I'm gonna get me a pig.' About ten guns will come flyin' across the bar. I'll just take 'em all!"

The laughter exploded again.

"All right, pipe down," Maraney bellowed. "I said knock it off!"

Chiodo was assigned to a team detailed to work in Central

Park. Uncomfortable in his costume, he left the station with two partners he had never met before. One of them, an older man named Ed Barnes, seemed preoccupied. Barnes spoke to his regular partner, a bluff, genial Irishman named Joe Murphy.

"Joe, you want to catch tonight?"

"Naw. We're good for the month. What do you want to do?"

"I thought I'd go see my chick."

"Okay, gimme the phone number."

Joe wrote down the number and let Barnes out of the car. Then, as they drove again, he acknowledged Chiodo's presence for the first time.

"Hey listen, kid, I guess you're okay, right?"

"Uh, what do you mean?"

Murphy responded with a flurry of questions. How long had he been in TPF? What was his academy graduating class? Where did he live? Where was he stationed? Brooklyn? Who did he know in Brooklyn? Chiodo had the uneasy feeling he was being grilled. But finally Murphy seemed satisfied. "Let's stop by my place," the Irishman said. "The wife'll fix us a couple of drinks."

Joe lived in the Bronx. Over drinks he grew expansive and talked about himself, his successes, his arrests, his bravery.

"I thought you decoy guys were always looking to catch," Chiodo said. He was restless, and the drink tasted flat. "How come we're not on the street tonight?"

"Yeah, we catch. But we've got enough numbers for the month."

"Gee, that's tough on me. I'm new to decoy. I want to make this outfit as a regular. I'm told that they add up your arrests at the end of the month, and the guys with the high numbers stay on. Right now, I need every collar I can get."

"We'll grab you something later tonight. We know where everything is."

Two hours passed before Murphy walked to the phone and dialed his partner. "Hey, you finished screwin'? This kid's looking for a collar tonight. . . . Yeah, yeah, I know that, but come on anyhow. You need the fresh air."

Central Park lay in the warmth of early summer. Heavy foliage made its dark pockets impenetrable. The shadowed nooks and hollows formed trysting places for lovers and stalking grounds for hoodlums. Muggers, purse snatchers and rapists found abundant cover. So swiftly did they strike that victims often had no chance to scream. But this night the park was no action. The decoy team spent an hour in the park and then abandoned it for a neighboring street where thieves delighted in pilfering goods from parked cars. The unmarked decoy car sat with its windows open and packages on the seat. Chiodo and his partners lurked in the shadows, but no one came for the bait. Finally a dark figure darted across the street. Joe Murphy went after the running young man and brought him down with a flying tackle. A large paper bag tumbled from the youth's arms and burst open in the street, spilling out a screwdriver, pliers and ten tape decks.

"Where'd you get this shit?" Murphy snapped.

"I just bought it, man."

Murphy turned to Chiodo. "You want a collar? Take this guy."

"For what?"

"Possession of stolen property."

"We're not even sure it's stolen."

"You got reasonable grounds. Lock him up. Screw him. It'll give you a collar."

"What you mean, lock me up?" said the youth. "Man, I ain't did nothing. Man, I—"

"Shut your fucking face."

"Hey, man, play square. You ain't got nothin' on me. I just bought that stuff from a dude around the corner."

"Yeah, yeah, I know. Get in the car."

At the precinct station the youth admitted the tapes were stolen. "Yeah, big deal, so I took 'em out of a car." Chiodo

59

booked him. At 2:00 A.M. he went home to bed. Five hours later he was up and dressed to take his prisoner to court. For lack of a complaining victim, Chiodo had him arraigned on a short affidavit. Then, determined to make a case, he dug into the precinct's UF 61 file, "Report of a Crime," and pulled out every unsolved theft of tape decks from cars for the past two months, 150 of them. For the next five days, on his own time, he chased down people who had lodged complaints. Not one could identify any of the tapes recovered by the decoy team. Chiodo could not even prove there had been a theft. The case was dismissed. Chiodo was disgusted. At the station house he made no mention of the fruitless legwork. Anybody can be a damn fool, he told himself, but you don't have to advertise it.

His phone calls to Petrelli were almost daily now. After all, he had made a collar on his first night out. Pounding a uniformed post, he chafed and longed for action. Then he received another call. It was July 13, 1969.

"Chiodo, report to Seven-one Precinct for decoy duty."

This time his partners were the veterans Mike Mulloy and Red Standard. But with their regular partner taking a night off, they decided to while away the time in Brooklyn Heights, a quiet, upper-middle-class section with a view of Manhattan across the water. The skyline was stunning, but Chiodo brooded. Mulloy had become famous for his decoy feats, which included rescuing an old couple from a burning tenement and bursting in on a pot party singlehandedly to arrest everyone in the place. "Holding twenty-one," he had radioed. "Send a bus." At least Mulloy was sympathetic.

"Look, guys, I need a collar tonight," Chiodo grumbled. "Man, I need a bust bad. There's nothing happening in this neighborhood."

Red Standard stared at him. "Okay, kid, you want a collar? We'll call in and get an assignment change. What do you think, Mike?"

"The Six-oh Precinct," Mulloy said. "Coney Island." He looked evenly at Chiodo. "You got balls, kid?"

"Yeah, I've got balls. Anyhow, I worked the Six-oh in uniform. Why?"

"Well, this will be a little different than uniform, but we'll get you a collar in no time."

In summer, Coney Island's masses jostled for breathing space. Hot weather brought fights and riots, muggings, assaults, shootings, rapes, armed robbery and petty thievery on a large scale. But this evening the beach was orderly. After an hour of fruitless idling, they walked down a side street from the beach, past a line of old, weathered wooden houses. Mulloy spotted an abandoned house with a shadowy entrance.

"Good view from the street," said Red Standard.

"Yeah, they'll see him real good."

"Okay," Standard said. "Have you got two bucks, Chiodo? Put 'em in your shirt pocket. You're gonna be a drunk, sleeping it off. Now do just what I tell you. Somebody approaches you, don't move. Keep your eyes shut, like you're unconscious, and don't move. Don't try to grab him or anything. Lie there like you're dead. Because if you don't, you might be. A couple of weeks ago one of our guys got a broken jaw doing this thing. Another man had his ribs kicked in. So don't be a hero. Mike and me, we'll be the heroes, understand?"

"I understand, but—"

"Do you want a collar tonight or don't you."

"I want a collar."

His partners vanished into the shadows.

Time seemed to drag. Half a block from where Chiodo lay sweating in the half-dark, Coney Island blazed in the night. Shrieking carnivalgoers spun wildly on the Himalaya ride, hair flying, lights streaking past them in a sickening blur. Hurdy-gurdy music mixed in mad counterpoint with blaring rock sounds, the cries of barkers, the hiss of surf and a roller coaster's rattling roar. Crowds flowed along the boardwalk amid warm smells of hot dogs, hamburgers and popcorn. Beaches, walkways and side streets bore the litter of crushed paper cups and rotting bits of discarded food. As Chiodo visualized these things, his sense of isolation grew.

The odor of decay thickened along these worn-out neighborhoods stretching back from the sea. The sandblasted wooden houses from another era clustered in the darkness along narrow streets; houses with long, dirty windows, overhanging roofs, peeling paint and fronts cut out to form entryways. Some were condemned and boarded up, empty but for the rats and human derelicts who sheltered within their sagging walls.

Chiodo sprawled on his back in the littered vestibule. Tension sharpened his senses. The stench of old urine, saturating a near wall, penetrated his nostrils. The edge of a warped plank dug into his back. His ears probed for tiny, alien sounds through the distant noise of the amusement park. Somewhere, a rat scuttled. A flake of plaster dropped from the ceiling. From the street came the sound of a passing car. His stomach grumbled. He cursed his fear.

Footfalls approached along the sidewalk. Voices murmured. Chiodo closed his eyes, listening. The footfalls stopped.

"Hey, look at that drunk. Go check, see what he's got in his pockets." It was the voice of a young black man.

"No, man." This was a black female. "You go check his pockets."

A third person spoke. Female. Probably white. "I'll do it."

Soft footsteps, now, drawing near. They stopped at his head. A hand touched his shirt pocket. "Hey," she whispered, "he's got money in there."

"Get it."

Chiodo's muscles tightened. Involuntarily, his eyes twitched. The girl jumped away.

"He's waking up."

"He ain't wakin' up," said the male voice. "Get the bread. If he moves, I'll break the motherfucker's head."

Chiodo fought down the impulse to make a lunge for them. But questions nagged his mind. What kind of a weapon did they

have? A blackjack? A heavy board? And where were his partners? Were they really hiding nearby, ready to jump in, or had
they decided to play a joke on him and go for beers? He felt the
frustrations of the blind.

The girl's hand rummaged in his shirt pocket and drew out
the two dollar bills. Then the footsteps retreated . . .

"Get 'em!"

Mike Mulloy's voice cracked like a shot. Chiodo's eyes flew
open, and he sprang to his feet, running. In a dozen loping
strides Mulloy caught the black youth and brought him up short
in a hammerlock. Red Standard raced after the black girl and
grabbed her around the waist. Chiodo pounded into the street
and seized the white girl by the shirt. She whirled and
screamed. "Damn you, scumbag son of a bitch, let me go!"
Fingernails slashed for his eyes, and an upthrust knee barely
missed his groin. He twisted her around, snapped her arm upward behind her back and locked her, spitting and screaming,
with an arm around the throat.

Moments later, a Transit Authority police car stopped. The
three prisoners, handcuffed, were shoved into the back seat for
the ride to the 61st Precinct station. Mulloy turned to Chiodo
and grinned.

"Okay, kid, you got your collar. Three of them."

Chiodo was elated.

It was quiet in the station. Upstairs, in the cage, Manuel
Ortega came awake lying facedown in his own vomit. *Madre
de Dios,* he said, and started to cry. Two detectives in the
squad room ignored him. Downstairs, Lieutenant Ed Marks
worked the desk. Eighteen years on the force; two more and
maybe he would retire. The desk rose high above the reception
area. Marks was known for the pride he took in his paper work.
The New York Police Department was a gigantic living entity
of men, machines and paper forms. Arrest sheets, booking
sheets, property sheets. If it weren't for men like Marks the

63

department would choke on it all. It had been a quiet evening. Ed Marks liked quiet evenings. He grunted contentedly and emptied the ashtray.

The door opened. In walked three handcuffed prisoners trailed by a scruffy trio of men with shields pinned to their shirts. Lieutenant Marks recognized Mike Mulloy and frowned.

"What have you guys got?"

"We've got a robbery, lou," said Mulloy. "These people took money from our decoy man."

"Call me 'Lieutenant Marks,' officer. Save that 'lou' shit for TPF lieutenants."

Marks stared at the white girl. She had creamy skin, brown eyes, auburn hair and wore a snug pink pullover, blue jeans and sandals. She returned his gaze. Her eyes were warm and gentle.

"Fuck your robbery," Lieutenant Marks said. "What is it, the old dollar-in-the-pocket trick? That's no arrest. Get the hell out of here with that bullshit."

Mulloy seemed unmoved. "Look, lou, either we book 'em here or I'll call Inspector Sullivan and he'll come down and book 'em."

"Son of a bitch!" The lieutenant stood up, flung down his pen, stalked away into a side office and slammed the door. They could hear him shouting something. The black youth snickered. Then the office door opened, and Marks, red-faced and still shouting, emerged with a captain who was trying to calm him.

"Okay, Ed, take it easy. Let's see about this." The captain faced Mulloy. "All right, what are the circumstances?"

"Captain, Patrolman Chiodo here was acting in a decoy capacity, lying down, and these two coaxed that girl to reach into his pocket and take two dollars."

The captain frowned. "Was the two dollars showing?"

"No, sir, the two dollars wasn't showing."

The captain turned to Chiodo. "You always carry two dollars in that pocket?"

"No, sir."

"Why was it there tonight?"

"I just thought I'd have two dollars handy, for ice cream."

The captain clenched and unclenched his fists. "We've warned you guys about making arrests like this in the Six-oh. I don't like 'em."

"Yeah," said Mulloy, "but Inspector Sullivan likes them."

"See what I mean!" shouted Marks. "I ain't taking this crap, captain. These bastards keep throwing Sullivan's name in my face. Fuck them and Inspector Sullivan."

The captain took Marks by the arm and ushered him back into the office, where the shouting gradually lost volume. Finally, Marks came back out, sat down at the desk and sighed. "All right, what are the prisoners' names?" He printed the names neatly. The black youth's eyes gleamed, fixed on the moving pen.

"Royal, Edward Simpson, nineteen, charged with larceny from the person . . ."

"That's P.L. one-five-five point two-five, lou," said Standard.

"Yeah, I know the Penal Law, smart-ass."

"Pigs," hissed Royal.

"What's that?"

"White píg motherfuckers." The face contorted. The voice rose into a choked cry. "White pig motherfuckers, you ain't taking me! You ain't taking me! You ain't taking me!"

Standard and Chiodo grabbed handfuls of belt and shirt and hustled him on tiptoes up the worn steps to the detective squad room and holding cages on the second floor. Royal screamed and struck his head against the wall. "Motherfuckers! White pig motherfuckers!"

"This guy's psycho," panted Standard.

"You guys are in big trouble," raged Royal as the door slammed shut in his face. "My uncle works for the mayor. I'm gonna get you guys fired, man."

In the drunk cage, Manuel Ortega began to sing. *"Cuando caliente el sol,"* Manuel sang, *"aqui en la playa . . ."*

Mulloy brought the two girls up the stairs. Abruptly Royal's shouting ceased and he fell to his knees in the cage. "I did it. I did it. The girls didn't do nothing."

"... *siento tu cuerpo vibrar, cerca de mi,*" Manuel sang.

A precinct detective appeared. "What have you guys got?"

"Robbery," Mulloy replied.

"What, the old dollar-in-the-pocket again?"

Mulloy reddened. "That's right," he snapped. "They're booked, so shut your mouth and mind your own business. We'll do the paper work. We don't need you."

A growl came from the detective's throat. He lunged at Mulloy, fists flailing. The decoy man ducked, and smashed the detective in the face. Two other detectives swarmed in from the next room and rushed Mulloy. They went down in a tangle, guns clattering from holsters. The girls screamed.

Blows thudded. "Ooof! Bastard."

"... *Es tu palpitar,*" Manuel sang, "*es tu cara ...*"

"White motherfucking pigs! My uncle'll have you arrested. Kill 'em. Kill the motherfuckers!"

"... *es tu pello, son dos besos ...*"

A lieutenant of detectives came running. "What the hell is this? Break this up. Cut it out!"

The combatants separated and scrambled to their feet, breathing hard.

"What's wrong with you guys, cops fighting cops?" shouted the lieutenant.

"Cops hell," spat Mulloy. "They're pimples on my ass."

"... *Cuando caliente el sol ...*"

"Somebody shut that guy up," bellowed the lieutenant.

The tension broke. Royal giggled hysterically. The girls laughed. Even the lieutenant had a smile on his face.

The detective went to the water fountain and washed blood from his mouth. Mulloy sat down grimly at a desk and began writing the arrest report. The white girl's manner, meanwhile, had changed from the shrieking, foulmouthed tigress she had

66

been on the street. Now she was subdued and polite. Her father was called and arrived at the station, a pale little man wringing his hands. "This is the third time she's been arrested. I don't know what we're going to do with her. She's only seventeen."

The following morning Chiodo took his charges to court for arraignment. Edward Royal turned out to be a fugitive from a mental hospital and considered extremely dangerous.

"We were lucky," Mulloy said. "Real lucky."

Chiodo thanked his partners for letting him take all three arrests. "You guys did all the work and I get all the credit."

Red Standard grinned. "Don't mention it, kid. You've got balls. We'll make sure the right people hear about it, too."

A week later, Patrolman Daniel Chiodo was assigned to the 18th Precinct of Manhattan South. Primary assignment: decoy duty.

5

The Death Merchants

Summer smothers the city. Even the evening sweats. The sun is slow to go down, and dusk lingers, softening the hard edges of drab tenements that hover like crones over their stoops. Heat radiates from the cement. Cooking odors waft from open windows. Men and women slump on stoops and fire escapes, waiting for the chance breeze. Yet the mood of the sidewalk loses none of its urgency. Always and unchanging, the sidewalk is a restless life. One cannot forget that just beneath its surface the East Village is a hunting ground. Strangely, too, one becomes attuned to it; the hunter of hunters develops extra sight. So it was with Chiodo. Decoy work was changing and maturing him.

Even this world, so bizarre and out of joint at first, had its patterns. For all the teeming streets, odd costumes, stringy hair, freaks and pseudofreaks and counterculture oddities, Chiodo had come to recognize the patterns and spot the breaks. Head shops, bathed in deep, pulsing lights and reeking of incense, belched their heavy music. Children of hippie couples ran ragged, panhandling. Everywhere there were bodies, walking and not walking, shaking and sweating or crumpled in the depths of morphine among the garbage cans. A break in the patterns was sensed rather than seen. Was there too much tension on the corners? Why did so many people go in and out of that tenement? Was this man walking too fast, or that one too slowly? Spotting the little deviations was part of the hunter's trade. Sometimes, too, one sought strange alliances.

"Look, I ain't jivin', man. It is a big drop." Dee, the informer, spoke in bursts. The eyes squinted and darted out of a face formed as if from a chunk of coal. The nose leaked, requiring frequent wipings. Grimy fingers prowled the lumps and crevices of the face, the body, the arms. "Man, this is on the square. I heard it real good. A black dude from uptown is making the drop. I hear he drives a white Buick. Eight o'clock, Avenue B and Sixth." Then he was gone, melting into the crowd.

Pat Mayhew was doubtful. "Bastard's probably lying, Chi."

Chiodo leaned against a broken iron railing. His black hair had grown longer and was caught in a red headband. The faded Army fatigue jacket hung loose, its back decorated with a peace symbol and the crudely inked slogan, "Ball for Peace." His blue jeans were ragged, and his sneakers scuffed and old. "Maybe, but it's worth a shot," he said. "What the hell, we're looking to catch, ain't we?"

It was a dirty business, but the street was a dirty world. You played by street rules, few of which had ever been taught in the academy. A few weeks earlier the decoy team had picked up Dee, the 23-year-old black junkie. Terrified by the threat of jail and the agonies of heroin withdrawal, he had turned informer. Chiodo had plans for Dee. With enough fear in his stomach, the junkie might lead them to John the Limp.

For 14 years the shrewd old pusher, nicknamed for his wooden leg, had dealt hard drugs from a run-down Broadway hotel. The Limp had protection from somewhere, for even the narcotics squad couldn't seem to nail him. Yes, The Limp would make a fine collar for the decoy team. But for now, something less would have to do. The drop was due at eight o'clock, Dee had told them. By 7:45 they had the corner staked.

In the street you had to blend. Chiodo was still surprised at how readily people accepted him for what he pretended to be: Chi, the hippie drifter, a nervous, watery-eyed squinter, loose and unstrung, obviously into drugs. The low-hanging fatigue jacket now concealed a small-frame Smith & Wesson .38, lighter and less bulky than the regular service revolver he had carried in uniform.

From the beginning he had adapted quickly to the street. Chiodo chuckled inwardly recalling his father's dismay at his scruffy growth of whiskers and lengthening hair. *"Marrone,"* groaned John Chiodo, "now he's becoming a bum!" But the disguise added an exhilarating new dimension to police work. If one looked his part, crime in the streets was not hard to find. Even working merely as a fill-in on the various three-man teams, his numbers took a sharp rise. They had gone after car boosters, flimflam men, muggers, mashers, robbers and petty thieves. They prowled lower Broadway and the Bowery, nabbing hoodlums in the act of beating and robbing street bums for pennies; they caught street-corner Romeos pawing women pedestrians and chased purse snatchers and junkies. But the old clothes and disheveled appearance also had disadvantages.

One night, accompanied by the big quiet Irishman John Banion, Chiodo saw a youth holding up a liquor-store clerk with a knife. They jumped the stocky, red-haired bandit, wrestled him to the floor of the store and were snapping on the handcuffs when, behind them, a rookie precinct cop barged in from the street swinging his nightstick. A blow cracked across Chiodo's collarbone. "Hey, we're cops!" he shouted. The rookie apologized profusely. "Dumb fuck," Chiodo fumed, rubbing his bruised shoulder, "what'd you think we were, Santa Clauses?"

Those months of reading laws and ordinances, many of them obscure, also were paying off. When a street-corner idler offered to sell him a worthless watch for $25, Chiodo put him under arrest.

"What's the charge, man?" asked his bewildered partner.

"Fraudulent accosting."

"Where'd you dig that one up? It's new to me."

"I read a lot."

Chiodo completed his first month with 13 arrests. His name shot to the top of the monthly performance lists along with that of the aggressive veteran Charlie Ficelli. The results were especially pleasing to Sergeant Joe Drackus, supervisor of the Manhattan South decoy unit. Drackus was a mild but demanding boss. His 30-odd men, of whom 18 were on duty in half a dozen teams during a typical evening, were expected to produce. Heavyset, jowly, in his middle thirties with thin, sandy hair and a small bemused smile, Drackus seldom raised his voice or laughed out loud. But as one of the original 75 members of the TPF, he took a fierce pride in the force and in his decoy men. But, as long as the numbers were high, he also could be surprisingly tolerant of small transgressions. Drackus knew that his men often pursued their private love lives while technically on duty, or sometimes flashed the shield to reserve a downtown hotel suite for after-hours parties and were notorious at making excuses for one another, but such was the burden he bore. "You bastards do your jobs," he told them, "and we'll have no problems."

On the night the new performance sheet was tacked to the bulletin board, Drackus's reaction was low key but, in its way, eloquent. "Chiodo, you're catching on fast."

Tom Blake and Pat Mayhew also had been transferred out of Brooklyn to Manhattan South. When the last decoy man had reported back to the station following the nightly duty tours, Chiodo often joined them for a drink at Killy's bar.

"Man, how the hell did you get into decoy so fast?" Blake wanted to know. "You must be related to Inspector Sullivan."

"I just got lucky."

"We heard about that bust for fraudulent accosting," said Mayhew. "With an attitude like that, you ought to work with us."

"Naw, you guys would grab all the collars."

"Hell, we'd make so many there'd be plenty to go around," said Blake. "Besides, we rotate the collars. When your turn comes up, you take 'em. But I'll tell you this, Chi. We don't pull no bullshit, flaking people. We don't believe in that."

"Great. I don't want to work with anybody who pulls that shit. I had an experience the other night that turned me off on a guy. Do you know Vinny La Rosa?"

"Yeah. Guinea guy. I never worked with him."

"Well, we were working the Village, and La Rosa sees a bunch of kids on a stoop. He knows one of them for a junkie. So we give 'em a toss and they're clean. Only he holds one of the kids and says, 'You're in.' The kid says, 'I'm clean.' La Rosa says, 'No, you're not clean. You dumped a hash pipe on me last week and I'm giving it back to you.' So he pulls this little hashish pipe out of his pocket, which he claims the kid had dropped a few nights earlier running away. It pissed me off. I tell him, 'Man, you're gonna let that kid go. You don't flake nobody when you work with me.' He says, 'Bullshit, I'm taking him.' I told the kid to get lost, and he took off. La Rosa was mad. He said, 'I'd like to bust your fucking head for letting that guy go.' I told him, 'Any time you're ready.' We didn't talk much after that."

"You ought to work with me and T.B. here, Chi," Mayhew said. "We'd make a good team."

"Okay, when do we start?"

"I'll talk to Drackus."

Drackus had put them together the following night, and since then the team had functioned remarkably well. Temperamentally, the fiery, pugnacious Blake and the quiet Mayhew were opposite extremes. Chiodo seemed to fit somewhere in the middle. As time passed in nightly street duty, primarily in the Village, they began looking to him more and more for balance and decisions. The canny Drackus, meanwhile, kept an eye on their steadily rising numbers and chuckled softly to himself.

Now they waited for a white Buick bearing a black dude from uptown and a delivery of heroin.

At the corner, a knot of Puerto Rican youths talked in Spanish. Down the block, Tom Blake lounged in his hippie clothes, watching. Pat Mayhew stood across the street, scratching himself. Chiodo drifted over to Mayhew.

"Do you want to take the guy in his car?" Mayhew said quietly.

"Might as well. The spics aren't going to hassle us for jumping a black guy. No use taking chances, though. Catch him in the car and take off with it. They'll think it's a mug job. . . ."

Something changed on the corner. The talk died. Mayhew peered over Chiodo's shoulder. "Uh-oh," he said. "Take a look."

A radio patrol car stopped at the curb. Two uniformed policemen got out and walked into the crowd. "All right, what're you guys doing on the corner? Who's carrying? What've you got?" They jerked hands to heads, spun people around and frisked. "Hey, man, I'm clean. I ain't got nothing. Nothing, man." Minutes dragged by. Satisfied, the policemen ordered the corner cleared and turned back to their car.

At the intersection, a white Buick slowed long enough for the driver to catch a glimpse of uniforms. It speeded up again. Chiodo watched the taillights vanish down the street.

"Damn!" Mayhew said. "Let's chase him and give him a toss."

"No. If we get on his ass, he'll just dump on us. We'll get him next time. Dee will give him up again. We'll lose it all with a chase."

"Let's go see our squeal."

The open window brought some light from the street, but no air. He had dragged the old mattress out from the wall to the middle of the room before shooting up. Somewhere a transistor radio played, "My time ain't long, baby. Oh, sweet thing, my time ain't long. . . ." He had the shakes. The matches kept going out; he had to use six of them to get the candle lit.

Dee got the bottle cap off the table and found the rusty tweezers to hold it with. Gently he tore open the glassine envelope, but started to shake again and had to put it down. A few drops of water into the bottle cap, and then the powder. Easy, easy. Both hands gripped the tweezers. The candle flame danced beneath the blackened bottle cap. In the light his eyes were two great orbs shining out of a black face. Sweat poured down the face, saturated the grimy T-shirt and soaked into the mattress. Then the mixture was bubbling.

The decoy men knew Dee's kind. He was too far gone even to hate anymore. Once he would have hated them all, the way he had hated in Harlem. An old knife scar slid down one side of his face, a reminder of Harlem. It was said that white pussy got him that, messing with a white junkie girl. She was Shark Eye's girl, and one night Shark Eye caught Dee in an alley and worked on his belly and his face with a knife while three others held him down. "Nigger, you lucky I don't cut your balls off," Shark Eye had said. "I see you around here one more time and I'm gonna cut them off and stuff them down your throat." And so Dee had left Harlem and come down to the Village. He had dragged the mattress off a junk pile and into the abandoned tenement, to live with the stinks and the roaches and the rats.

You could make a connection fast in the Village, as fast as in Harlem, only the shit wasn't as good. They had better-grade stuff in Harlem. So Dee was shooting up twice a day and working the streets in between, stealing to feed the habit. The decoys caught him right after he had grabbed an old woman's purse and made a buy. Chiodo slammed him against a wall until his teeth rattled, and threatened to bust him. Just thinking about jail made a man like Dee want to vomit. Twice before, they knew, he had gone cold turkey in jail, with the shaking, the vomiting, the pain. Now the decoys helped him to survive and he didn't have to grab pocketbooks and roll drunks. Only now he lived with a deeper, colder fear, a fear as big as the Shark Eye fear. The street had eyes and ears. A squeal did not last long.

He waited for the mixture to cool and dropped in a wad of cotton. The needle was taped to a medicine dropper with a rubber bulb. The needle took the fluid. He knotted the old towel around his left arm and twisted. The vein popped up beneath a mass of needle scars. He was shaking again. The needle pierced the skin. Gently, gently, he squeezed the bulb, then eased off to get a little blood, then squeezed again. It flowed in. "Honey, honey," throbbed a voice from somewhere, "I need your love so fine. . . ."

He was nodding out as they walked in, a dark shape sprawled on a filthy mattress beside the guttering stub of candle. "Wake him up!" Pat Mayhew nudged the body with his foot. "All right, get up. Get your ass out of there!" Dee's eyes fluttered and he came up slowly, like a man swimming. Chiodo hauled him to his feet by the belt.

"What's this bad info you gave us about the drop?" Chiodo snarled. "Are you trying to fuck with us, bastard?"

Dee fought to focus his eyes. "Wha-what you talking about, man. I gave it to you straight. Didn't he show?" The words were heavy and slurred.

"Yeah, a white Buick showed up, and so did a patrol car. You're tipping off them uniformed humps, too." Chiodo shook him by the shoulders. "We don't like it when you pull that shit on us."

"Let's lock him up," growled Blake.

"I'd rather bust his face in."

"Hey, Dee, hold your arm out," said Blake. "I'm going to cure your habit, mother."

Dee's eyes rolled, and he started to tremble. "Look, I don't know nothin' about what happened, man. Give me another chance. I'll make it up to you tomorrow. Tomorrow, man, I'll give you somethin' real good."

"There ain't no tomorrow, motherfucker."

Chiodo pushed, and the loose body toppled backward onto the mattress. Mayhew grabbed one of the man's arms and held it out straight. "Go ahead, Chi, give him the big one."

Dee's face contorted. "NO! Look, please don't. Don't, man, please! There's this Spanish guy, see. He's been carryin' a lot lately. Lemme go find him. I'll take you right now. I'll go find him."

Chiodo glanced at Mayhew and Blake. They nodded. "Okay," he said, "but you mess up one more time and you're going away. You hear me, junkie? You hear me?"

"I ain't gonna cross you, man."

"All right, where do we go?"

"There's this apartment house on East Eighth. Them guys, they hangs out around the front, and the spic, he's dealin'. So I'll take the cigarette lighter you give me and go looking. If he's there and he's carryin', I'll signal you with the big flame when you drives around the block."

"Okay, let's go."

If daytime in the city of New York had become treacherous, night was a peril. Even the old people who had spent their lives in a neighborhood were reluctant to go out after dark. Robbery, murder, muggings and rape surged as the sun went down. While the decoy units had been created to catch street thugs in the act, drugs were at the root of 80 percent of violent street crime and were closely interwoven with prostitution. The merchants of death and the sellers of flesh worked hand in hand. If decoy men could not always lure the violent criminal by the ruse of disguise, then they certainly could go after one of the prime causes of the city's madness. On the monthly TPF tally, after all, a drug arrest was as good as any other. And while they worked against the same administrative handicaps as regular undercover narcotics agents—notably, the city's refusal to provide money with which to make buys—the decoys saw their drug-arrest totals rising each month. For Chiodo this had become a source of grim satisfaction.

"See anything yet?"

From the back seat of the unmarked Chevy, Tom Blake peered at the shadowy group on the stoop of a brick tenement. It was their second pass around the block. The murmur of voices was broken by laughter.

"Not yet," Mayhew replied. "Let's take another . . . Wait. There it is!"

The bright flame of a butane cigarette lighter flared in the group. Chiodo eased the car to the curb, and the three slid out, pinning shields to their shirts. They moved in fast. "Okay, everybody inside. Into the hall, you. Move! Up against the wall and spread 'em. Stand still. Nobody move a muscle."

Eight sullen faces turned to the wall between raised arms. While Chiodo stood back, hand on his pistol butt, Mayhew and Blake patted them down swiftly—shirts, waists, trouser legs, ankles, armpits—and then backed away, puzzled. "Nobody's carrying," Blake muttered. "No bulges, no lumps, nothing." One by one they pulled each suspect aside, slapping and cuffing. "All right, who's got it? Who's carrying?" Still nothing. To protect the informer, Dee received the same treatment.

"Which one?" hissed Chiodo. The junkie indicated a swarthy, thickset Puerto Rican. "Okay," Chiodo sighed, "we'll try again."

The second search also was fruitless. The decoy men let them go.

A short time later, Dee appeared at a prearranged meeting place. He held out two packets of heroin in the familiar glassine envelopes. "From the spic," he said.

"Damn," growled Mayhew.

They went back to the stoop. Four idlers were still there, including the Puerto Rican. Again the herding into the hallway, the shouting and cuffing. Nothing. They separated the man Dee had identified.

"Strip him," Mayhew said.

Taped inside his boxer shorts were 36 packets of heroin, worth three dollars apiece on the street. "Man," grunted Blake, "you sure go in for expensive underwear."

They shoved him, handcuffed, into the car. On the ride to the station, the prisoner looked out at the passing street with hooded eyes. "I know who gave me up," he said evenly. "He's dead."

The next afternoon the decoy men walked into their informer's tenement and warned Dee. The black man's face seemed to turn to stone. "If he even thinks it's me, man, then I ain't going to be on the street long."

"You'd better disappear for a while."

Dee shrugged.

As they walked back into the street, Chiodo frowned. "If he doesn't take our advice, he's gone. The bastard ain't worth saving, but he's been a pretty good squeal."

"Hell, Chi, you know how it is," said Mayhew. "Killing a junkie is easy as taking a breath. This shit they sell in the Village, it's got maybe two grams of smack mixed in with the milk sugar and crap. In Harlem you got around four grams. No matter. When the pusher wants to knock a guy off, he slips him a deck that's got twelve grams. Wham!"

"It's one of the things that really galls my ass," said Blake. "You hear these bleeding hearts talking about rough cops. 'Be nice. Be nice.' But if there's any democracy in the streets, I haven't found it. The pusher, he's judge, jury and executioner. A junkie don't even dare make his chick mad at him. She'll go to the man, whispering, 'He's turning you in.' Next thing, you find the guy stiffed out in a basement. O.D."

They did not see Dee for three weeks. Maybe he had taken the warning and disappeared. But one day they went to the tenement and started up the stairs. At the second landing, Mayhew choked and held his nose. "Whew!" They turned around, walked back down and called the Rescue Squad. Wearing gas masks, the rescue men brought down the remains in a rubber sack.

Dee had been dead for at least a week. This was September 20, so they guessed that it had happened about the 12th or 13th.

78

There were no mourners. Dee had been part of a system, and the system stank. Besides, Chiodo was beginning to view passing events with detachment. For a policeman, after all, detachment was a functional necessity. Even during those months of emergency street duty before his graduation from the academy, he had begun to acquire a thicker skin. At the scene of an accident, with a shattered car containing a screaming mass of flesh in the back seat and a bloody remnant in the front, one could not be squeamish. As a private citizen he would have vomited; on duty he radioed for the ambulance, administered first aid, directed traffic, saw that the wreckage was cleared and wrote up a report, mechanically, before knocking off for lunch. As for the informer, Dee, he had been executed by his own kind for violating the law of the street jungle.

What Chiodo regretted most, ironically, was missing a crack at John the Limp. His partners shared the feeling. They knew that the old street veteran ran a profitable business in heroin, distributing to pushers and dealing direct to carefully selected users. Undoubtedly, Dee had been an occasional customer. And who knows? Perhaps his last lethal shootup had been supplied through The Limp. One evening, as the decoy team changed clothes at the station house, Mayhew grew thoughtful. "We'll get his ass yet," he said.

Night closed over Washington Square. Heavy traffic rushed through streets glistening from a brief shower. Hippies, drifters and prostitutes strolled the square, ignoring camera-slung tourists, hurrying young executives clutching folded copies of the *Wall Street Journal* and secretaries in maxiskirts, out for a night on the town.

Chiodo idled in the square, brooding. Even though his roots were here, he was becoming aware that he hated the city. "No place on earth," he had told Mayhew earlier, "has got such a sick mix of humanity." But even as he said it, he couldn't buy it all. New York was too complex. The Village, for example, had given him stark glimpses of the ugliness of man and yet, at the same time, a deeper insight into counterculture people. Among the adherents of naturalism, one found those who truly attempted to renounce materialism and greed for lives of gentle simplicity. He even had to admit that there was a certain pleasure to padding the streets in his strange clothes, playing a part. Weren't they all, in one way or another, renegades? Hadn't he, Dan Chiodo, given up a good-paying job and secure future to prowl the streets in his long hair and bizarre costume, posing as a junkie and yet hunting for human game?

Perhaps they all had a role to play. What else lured boys and girls from comfortable middle-class and wealthy homes to drop out into a world of make-believe? Why would bank clerks, lawyers, young executives and stock clerks spend weekdays in prim respectability at their jobs and then rush to the Village on Friday evenings for a weekend of the hippie life, wearing faded jeans, love beads, sneakers and wigs to cover their short hair? In its way, the system used them all—sometimes brutally. The drug trade reaped lush profits in heroin, cocaine and marijuana, picking the pockets of those renouncing greed. Even the symbols of counterculture, the beads and sandals, the belts and bracelets, went at outrageous prices, paid for out of monthly checks from the folks back home. And if tragedies were to be counted, what of the legions of starry-eyed girls who landed each day in the big city, eager to make their way, only to be snared in the webs of dope and prostitution? Often enough it started with a rape and ended in bondage to one of the ruthless pimps who drove Eldorados with leopard-skin tops, sported about in spiffy mod clothes and high-heeled boots, took a huge cut of the prostitute's fees and was not above murdering the girl who crossed him and dumping her body in an alley.

It was part of the system, and the system stank. And here he was, the Sicilian supercop who was supposed to help bring law to the streets. Bring law to these streets? Hah! It was like facing a stampede with a slingshot. . . .

"Hey, man, you looking for some good shit?"

80

The face was young and lean. The eyes shifted nervously. The voice had the hush of the practiced conspirator. God, he looked young. Seventeen? Eighteen? Somewhere there was an Italian mother with a pan of cold spaghetti on the stove, sitting in her apron on a flowered, overstuffed chair, worrying.

"Yeah," said Chiodo, affecting his squint. "What've you got?"

"What do you want?"

Chiodo glanced over his shoulder. Somewhere back there his partners were trailing. Was that Blake at the lamppost? He could not be sure. "I dunno. See, I'm into everything. Grass, powder, you name it. That's how it is, man."

"I can turn you on to some heavy stuff. Come with me to Broadway."

Chiodo fell into step beside him, and they walked to Broadway. The youth stopped, sweating and fidgety. Chiodo recognized the symptoms. His pusher needed a fix. "What do you want?" the kid asked.

Chiodo twitched the corner of his mouth and wiped his nose. "Get me a couple decks."

"Okay, that's ten bucks. Gimme five now and the rest when I come back with the shit."

The price of a deck in this neighborhood was three dollars. Obviously he intended to buy heroin for himself and never come back. Chiodo hedged. "No. Listen, man, I'll stay here. You get me the shit and I'll pay you when you come back."

"You gotta give it to me now."

"Fuck you, man, I ain't giving you nothing. Forget it." Chiodo turned to walk away. Behind him, a voice shouted at the edge of hysteria.

"Give me the bread now, or I'll kill you!"

He stood there, eyes blazing, wielding a heavy board from a broken fence. Chiodo spun and dashed for the corner of a building. As feet pounded in pursuit, he flattened against the wall and drew the .38. The pistol was aimed head-high as the youth turned the corner.

"Freeze or I'll blow your head off. I'm a cop. Hands in the air!"

The board clattered to the sidewalk as Mayhew and Blake came running across the street, dodging traffic.

His name was Lew Chasso. At age 19 he was already on five years' probation for selling narcotics. As Mayhew snapped on the handcuffs, he began to plead. "Man, don't take me, please. Give me a break."

"I'll give you a break," Chiodo said. "I'll break your fucking head."

"Come on, man, you help me and I'll help you."

It was a good time to fire the question. "Do you know John the Limp? Pegleg John?"

The eyes dropped. The face grew expressionless. "No, I don't know no Pegleg John."

Chiodo shrugged. "Then forget it."

"Look, man, I don't know him."

Chiodo grabbed him by the throat. "Look, prick, you do know him. We want John the Limp."

"I can't give up John!"

It was the opening they needed. Blake took the long route to the station while Chiodo and Mayhew put pressure on Chasso. Was John the Limp worth five years in jail? Was he worth cold turkey? Was he worth being thrown to the old cons, like so much fresh meat, in prison? And it would be five years and then some, they would swear to that. Five years plus a rap for attempted assault on a police officer and attempted sale. Chasso weakened, panic in his eyes. At the precinct station he was booked with the promise that they would help him all they could if he cooperated. Chasso cursed. Chiodo stalked out of the room. Blake took over the interviewing then, playing the role of a kindly uncle.

"Look, son, I want to tell you something about my partner out there, Chi. This guy might seem bad to you, but let me tell you, he really *is* bad. He's crazy. He'd kill you, and it wouldn't bother him a bit. He'd go to church Sunday morning and say a prayer for your dead ass. That's how mean he is. I'm not even sure you're going to court. He might decide to kill you tonight."

"He can't do that. I'm booked."

Blake patted him on the shoulder. "There are ways, son. An overdose. Take care of you. He'd just say you had some powder hidden on you that we didn't get. Too bad."

Chasso sat in silence, blinking. Around him, the cluttered old office of the precinct station was as cheerless as a pillbox. The walls brooded down upon him, and the air was close. His eyes shifted to the windows, covered in steel mesh, the battered desks and chairs, the old, nicotine-stained ashtray.

"All right," he said, "I'll do whatever you say."

Chiodo already had his plan. "Here's what you do, Chasso. I want you to call The Limp. Tell him you're sick, in a bad way. You've got a friend who'll come over and pick up some powder, and please sell it to him. Then describe me. Got that?"

He made the call. The terror in his voice made the plea convincing. "Man, I'm about to die. I need it bad. . . . Yeah, he's a buddy of mine. . . . Black hair, red headband, old fatigue jacket with a peace symbol. On the jacket it says, 'Ball for Peace.' He's got a beard, black beard. . . ." John the Limp agreed to meet Chiodo at midnight.

At that hour the neighborhood around Pegleg's hotel was dark, desolate and terribly lonely. Deserted factories, warehouses and commercial buildings loomed over the street. Even the weight of the pistol on Chiodo's hip, and the awareness that his partners lurked in the shadows, did not reassure him. He stood shivering as the hand on his watch crept past 12:00, to 12:03, to 12:05. At last, a heavyset black man with a wooden leg came stumping slowly out of the hotel. Chiodo sniffed, wiped his nose with a sleeve and squinted in the dim light. "You John?"

"What do you want?" The voice was deep, guarded.

"Lew called you. Lew's bad sick. He needs some shit. He said—"

"How much shit?"

"F-four decks. We need four decks, him and me." Chiodo's face twitched.

John the Limp's eyes had a penetrating glitter. Was it a trick of the light? They seemed to bore holes into Chiodo. "You got the bread? Sixteen bucks."

"I got the bread."

"All right, come on upstairs."

That was it, the crucial point. The shrewd old Pegleg never dealt in the street, always in his room. If they took him, it would have to be here, outside.

Warily, Chiodo stepped back a pace. "No, man, I ain't going to no room. Once I tried to make a buy that way and got my ass beat in. I don't deal in no room. Go to hell. I'll get my shit someplace else."

"What's the matter with you? Didn't the kid tell you I'm good?"

"Fuck you and the kid. I'll take care of myself." He backed away. "I don't care if he dies."

Chiodo turned to leave.

"Hey, wait a minute."

"No, man," Chiodo was shouting now. "I ain't going to no room!"

The Pegleg stumped after him. "Shut up, shut up. I'll get your shit. Wait right here. Just wait, man. I'll be back in a few minutes."

He vanished into the hotel. Chiodo's hands were sweating. A hard knot tightened in his stomach. He glanced around for his partners. They were not to be seen. No movement disturbed the shadows. Twenty minutes went by. Chiodo agonized. The smart old bastard had made him for a cop. He had seen through it all. No wonder they couldn't catch him; he had a sixth sense. Chiodo was ready to walk away.

The wooden leg came clumping back. Chiodo took a deep breath and let it out, slowly.

"Okay, you got the bread?"

"I got it, man." Chiodo held out two dollar bills. "Here's a couple here and . . . let's see, I got a twenty. You got some change?"

Someone came walking along the sidewalk. Chiodo cringed and backed away, whimpering. "It's the man. Oh, God, it's the man. We're gonna get busted!"

"Be cool," the Pegleg hissed. "Be cool, you dumb junkie. It's not the man. Shut up."

A middle-aged white man in work clothes walked by, ignoring them. The footfalls quickly faded and were gone.

"You sure he's not watching us?"

"Yeah, man, I'm sure. Give me the twenty."

"No. Give me the shit and my change first."

The Limp was losing patience. "Shut up and give me the twenty. I got to go into the hotel for change."

"Let me see the shit first. You got the shit?"

The Limp opened his left hand. Four glassine envelopes glistened in the palm. The hand closed. "Now give me the twenty."

"All right." Chiodo reached back for his billfold. His fingers closed over the pistol grip. The .38 leaped from its holster and then was aimed, barrel shaking, at the broad, flat nose. "You're under arrest."

Shock burst over the face of John the Limp. Mayhew and Blake rushed from their hiding places.

"What do you mean, under arrest? You ain't no cop. You guys are tryin' to rip me off."

"I'm a cop. You don't move. You move, I'll kill you."

"Which hand?" Blake shouted.

"Left hand."

Blake, a powerful man in his twenties, grabbed The Limp's hand and tried to pry open the fingers. They locked shut as if made of steel.

"Open that hand!"

"Man, leave me alone."

Mayhew gave the wooden leg a sweeping kick. The stocky black man crashed to the sidewalk. Still the left hand remained clenched. The right hand made a darting move. Chiodo's eye caught the glint of a knife.

"Watch the knife!"

Mayhew stepped on the right arm, and the knife clattered free, an ugly K-55 honed razor sharp. Chiodo and Mayhew grappled for the heroin. Blake picked up the knife and pressed it to The Limp's stomach.

"If you don't open that hand," he hissed, "I'm gonna cut open your belly."

"Don't cut me, man. Don't cut me!" But the left hand remained clamped shut. Soundlessly, the K-55 flashed again. The shirtfront fell open, and a long streak of blood oozed from the skin. "Ohhh!"

The hand flew open.

The arrest of John the Limp stirred flurries of talk among the other decoy teams. Even though he was quickly released on bond, the prestige of Chiodo, Blake and Mayhew soared. But even as they basked in attention, Chiodo worried about the fate of Chasso. If he went free to await trial, the boy was in mortal danger. In jail he was reasonably safe, and they might be able to have him committed to a treatment program. "This kid is smart," Chiodo told his partners, "and he's not too far gone to be saved."

Chasso's bond was set at $5000. Chiodo went to visit the boy's mother, a tiny, birdlike woman rearing four children alone in a crowded fourth-floor walkup filled with chintz, china, gaudy pillows and a large picture of the Blessed Virgin. She did not weep.

"Ah, I've already cried all my tears over that boy. He is a good boy, so smart. It's this lousy neighborhood, and people he fell in with. If I even mention it he gets mad and runs out of the house."

Chiodo advised her to leave the boy in jail. "It's safer for him there, and maybe we can get some treatment. He needs a fresh start."

"I will do as you say."

But she could not leave him behind bars. A visit to her son, weeping and trembling, was too much. "I'm sick, momma. Oh, God, don't leave me here. They won't do nothing for me, momma. I need medicine." His tears dampened the front of her dress. Mrs. Chasso went to her savings. That afternoon her son was free.

In the weeks that followed, the decoys saw him twice. The first time he was being beaten by three street toughs in an alley. Chiodo, Mayhew and Blake waded in with fists and knees. Two attackers were left moaning and spitting blood, the third fled. Chiodo pulled Chasso out of the alley. "Go home, you stupid bastard. Go home and stay there." The boy promised to stay away from the street. But a few evenings later, as they cruised in the car, the police radio signaled a disturbance half a block away. "Man running with a knife." They answered the call. Chasso was racing on foot along the crowded sidewalk. Behind him came a dark, Spanish-looking man waving an open switchblade. Chiodo tackled Chasso, but the knife wielder eluded Chiodo's partners in the crowd. This time they took Chasso into protective custody and locked him up.

John the Limp's case dragged through repeated postponements. Finally he was permitted to plead guilty on a lesser charge of attempted possession of heroin. Penalty: three months in jail. Chiodo was stunned.

"Ain't this a bitch? We'd have done better charging him with jaywalking. How the fuck can you 'attempt to possess'? You either possess it or you don't."

At Chasso's hearing, the prosecutor refused to agree to a voluntary commitment for treatment of drug addiction. The judge revoked the probation. Chasso went to prison for five years. Later, as they prepared to go on duty, Mayhew eyed the grim-faced Chiodo.

"You want to catch tonight, Chi, or what?"

"Fuck it," Chiodo said. "Let's go get a drink."

That night, Decoy Team Three made no arrests.

6

Susie's Pad

Buckets snapped his fingers and rocked his head, watching the human flow. The beat was in his mind. Even when Buckets was not turned on, which was rare, the music was inside him. It went with the pulse of the street, the crowds, the cars, the lights, the darks and stinks of the city.

"Hey, man."

"Chi."

They wiped palms. Chiodo folded his lean body onto the stoop beside Buckets. The evening was coming on cool. To the west, beyond the rooftops, a vermilion smear was all that remained of the day. Chiodo sniffed, wiped his nose and turned up the collar of his fatigue jacket.

"How's it go, Buckets?"

"Yea, verily, with a little help from my friends." Rock, rock went the head. "Everything's up, man." The eyes darted beneath hooded lids. Across the street something undulated in skintight green. The eyes locked on the girl until she turned the corner and vanished. "Yea, verily." The eyes shifted again, seeking another target.

"Hey, uh, I hear there's a bash tonight." Chiodo made it sound casual. "Chick named Susie, her pad. You heard about it?"

Buckets pursed his lips and whistled tunelessly. The fingers snapped. Tangles of black hair flopped against his forehead. Chiodo leaned back, elbows on the step behind him, and waited.

"Uh-huh," Buckets said.

"You goin'?"

"Goin' where?"

"To Susie's pad?"

A knot of Puerto Ricans drifted past them, thumbs hooked in belts, walking tall. A lank, hollow-eyed hippie wearing a toga crossed the street. His feet were sandaled and his hair was a scarlet mass, shaped and set into a massive Afro. The eyes peered at them from dark shells. A bony hand thrust out. "Got some change, brother?" Chiodo shook his head. The mouth dropped into a sneer. "Fuck you, man." And he was gone.

"Believe it, man," Buckets said. "I'm taking my chick. She digs a good head group. Why?"

"Nothing special. I heard some guys rapping about it. I don't know this chick Susie. But me and my buddy got nothing doing and I figured we'd drop in, you know? I figured if you were tight with this chick, though . . . Well, we don't want to crash."

Buckets thought about it. Traffic moved past the stoop. Cigarettes glowed in the darkness. From a doorway came the sound of smashing glass and running feet. Somewhere a pianist was practicing scales. "Yeah," Buckets said. "I dig, man. Okay."

Chiodo finished his smoke, stood up and dusted off his pants. "Catch you later, Buckets."

"Sure. Uh, Chi?"

"Yeah?"

"I need to get me some shit. You carrying?"

90

"Naw."

"That's tough."

The fingers resumed their snapping.

Tom Blake was waiting at the alley. "Well?"

"Okay, it's all set."

Blake peeled the wrapper from a stick of gum and leaned against the building. "Chi, are you sure you want to go up there?"

"What do you mean, 'sure'?"

"Going into the party. You're always saying we shouldn't go inside without a warrant. You know what Drackus said about staying in the street."

"Fuck Drackus. We're invited in. Who needs a warrant? We're just going to a party, that's all. Besides, the communication says there's a lot of traffic in and out of that building at all hours. Them people ain't going in to eat doughnuts."

Blake nodded. "What time do we make it?"

"Around ten, ten thirty. By the time it's going real good they won't be too particular about who comes in."

They walked, sensing the vibrations of the street. It had become a familiar pulse to Chiodo now. As the months passed, he felt himself blending more and more into the speech, the idiom, the thoughts of the street. At home Linda had sensed the change. His mother had quarreled with him about it. "What has happened to your language? You didn't used to talk like this. We get you an education to talk English good, and your words are from the gutter." He couldn't help it. The profanity, the slang, the cynicism of the street had seeped into his bones like the dirty air. Even in some of the station houses they viewed the decoy cops as something alien, not fully acceptable in the normal police world. As time went on he was feeling less and less willing to be acceptable. They lived and played by different rules, and out here the rule was to blend, be part of it, survive.

The isolation was becoming troublesome, too. When a man pinned on the shield it was more than a badge; it became a barrier as well. Old friends of the civilian world were dropping away. On and off the job he found himself more and more in the company of other policemen. At the party last week Linda had chafed. "All you do is talk cop talk. Isn't there anything else?" But she understood. At purely civilian functions (strange, he no longer considered himself "civilian"), even family gatherings, he was different. They always introduced him now by his occupation. "This is Dan, the cop." Other people were simply Joe or Ed or George, but he was Dan the cop. A cop was something not quite human, a cop was authority, and he had to admit that he derived a certain enjoyment from it. There was less enjoyment, though, to the inevitable turn in party conversation, the undercurrents of animosity and suspicion one found there. What was it George had said? The cop was going to give him a ticket so he slipped him five bucks and went on his way. "If it had been me that stopped you," Chiodo had said, "your fat ass would be in for attempted bribery." The room fell silent, and then the subject abruptly changed. Later, Linda had been angry. Why did he say that to George? He had known George practically all his life. The matter had simmered between them all the way home.

"Hey, man—" Blake was talking to him. "—you gone deaf?"

"Huh?"

"How many times I got to ask you for a match?"

At 10:27 P.M. Chiodo, Blake and John Banion, their fill-in partner for the night, sat in a battered Volkswagen bus decorated with flowers and peace symbols. Banion handed the two-way Motorola to Blake, who put it on his belt beneath a loose-fitting shirt.

"John, you stay outside," Chiodo said, "and Tommy and me, we'll go in. If it's nothing but a pot party we'll leave, but if any hard stuff comes in we'll take the joint."

Banion's big Irish face drooped. "I don't like it. We're not supposed to be inside. You two maniacs are going to get our asses in a sling."

"Don't worry, John. Just be cool and stay outside."

Banion nodded.

Tom Blake had changed from a sport shirt and dungarees to his patched bell-bottoms, a floppy flowered shirt with the sleeves cut out, and a large leather peace medallion. Chiodo was in his customary frayed fatigue jacket, jeans and sneakers. As they walked into the Seventh Street tenement, Banion melted into a patch of shadow behind them.

The stairway was dark and reeked of mold and old cooking odors. Rotting floorboards sagged beneath their feet. From the sounds upstairs, the party was in full swing. At the second floor landing Chiodo knocked on 2-B. The door opened slightly, the night chain still attached, and a man's eye looked them up and down.

"Hi," Chiodo said, trying to talk above the noise.

"What do you want?" The voice was not friendly.

"We came to dig the bash, man."

"Sorry, this is a private happening."

"Yeah, I can dig it, man. But we got an invite. This is Susie's gig, right?"

"You know Susie?"

"Susie and me are tight, man."

The eye vanished. "Hey, Susie. There's a couple dudes here say they know you." Another eye came to the door, this one brown and warm, and made a quick appraisal. Then a soft female voice said, "I don't know you guys."

"Hey, babe, sure you do. I was digging you one night at Manny's. Then there was, let's see, the Electric Circus, I think. Sure—"

"I don't know you guys."

Chiodo turned to his partner. "Too bad, Tom, I guess Buckets was full of shit. Let's split."

"You know Buckets?" said the female voice.

"Buckets said for us to come over."

"Hey, Buckets. A dude out here says he knows you."

A new eye came to the door, peeping out from beneath a

93

hooded lid. Then Buckets spoke. "Yeah, that's my man from Saint Marks. Let him in. He's a head. Let him in. Come in, Chi."

The door closed, the chain rattled, the door swung open.

Sound smashed their ears. It came from a 100-watt stereo in the corner, turned up full. Smoke filled the room, sharp, penetrating, familiar. Blankets covered the windows, and bits of newspaper stuffing peeped out from cracks in the door, trapping the smoke. People were shouting and giggling. Couples swayed to the music, some of them nude. Lights flashed to the beat, lurid reds and purples, painting the walls with twisting silhouettes. Tom Blake's eye fixed upon a full-breasted girl, face contorted, streaming sweat, dancing alone to a pulsating rhythm.

"Go, baby, go," Tom Blake whispered.

It was a standard tenement flat with high, narrow windows, sagging furniture from some secondhand shop, tasseled lamps, worn carpet and soiled wallpaper. The occupants, whoever they were, had tacked mod posters to the walls: an oversize photoprint of W. C. Fields leering down from beneath his stovepipe hat, and a pregnant Girl Scout looking sad-eyed over the legend "Be Prepared." A narrow hallway led to two bedrooms and a bathroom to their left; to the right lay a dining alcove and kitchen.

The crowd might have been any party crowd, but looser. People clustered in corners, talking and laughing. All wore hippie clothes and long hair, and there was a smell of unwashed bodies. Chiodo wondered wryly how many of the males covered their short hair with shaggy wigs and dabbled in this life to break the tedium of staid, middle-class jobs uptown. Scratch one of the free-spirited girls, he mused, and you would find a Bryn Mawr runaway or a dropout from the Newport sailboat crowd, subsisting on weekly checks from daddy in Philadelphia. And daddy didn't give a damn.

At first no one gave them welcome. Even Buckets, having made possible their entry, now ignored them. It was Steve, a

94

casual acquaintance from the street, who made the first friendly overture. He wandered out of the crowd and sat down on the floor. "Hey, man, ain't this great? They're handing out some good shit. Really blow your mind, man."

"Who's treating?"

"Got a big daddy here. He's giving it away."

A bare-breasted girl worked through the crowd, accepting caresses and handing out ready-rolled joints from a cigar box. "Touch me. Touch me," she giggled. Her eyes were glazed. Tom touched her, and she handed each of them a joint.

Steve watched them light up and smoke. Under the steady scrutiny, Chiodo felt uncomfortable. He tried to fake inhaling and merely held the smoke in his mouth, but choked.

"Hey, man, don't let any of that stuff get away," laughed Steve.

"Got a sore throat," Chiodo said. This time he inhaled. The sharp, hot smoke caught in his lungs. Oh, what the hell. He held it and exhaled slowly.

"Ain't that good, man?"

"Yeah."

Steve left them.

The time passed. They watched, unspeaking, while the cigarettes burned down. Chiodo's eyes were smarting, and his throat burned. Merely breathing the air in the smoke-filled room would have been enough. A slight euphoria began taking hold of him. Concentrate, boy, he told himself. Somewhere he had read that concentration would overcome the effects of marijuana, but it didn't seem to work out that way. Steve came back with two bobby pins. Wordlessly they slipped the burning butts into the pins and dragged in smoke. The glowing tip of the roach burned Chiodo's lip.

Someone passed him a gallon wine jug, half full. Suddenly he had a consuming thirst. He gulped wine gratefully. The cool liquid washed his hot throat, and some of it dribbled into his beard. Chiodo giggled. Tiny flecks of light were swimming before his eyes, and the room contracted. The music took on a living quality, beating deep inside him. Someone was tugging at his arm. He looked up into the belly and breasts of Susie. She had removed her clothing, but the sight of her seemed more natural now. His eyes focused on her mouth. The mouth was full and red with tiny golden fuzz on the upper lip. Funny, he hadn't noticed the fuzz before. Beautiful fuzz. The lips grew large. The lips moved, and sounds came out. "Come and dance. Dance with Susie, you black-bearded devil. Dance with Susie, black-bearded devil."

Chiodo squeezed his eyes shut and shook his head. It was like shaking a bowling ball. Come out of it, come out of it, out of it, outofit, out . . . He opened his eyes and Susie was gone. He forced himself to look around. Other people were removing their clothes. Clothing littered the floor. Chiodo swung his vision around to his partner. Blake's eyes were red and fixed on a moving shape to his left. The shape was Susie, moving to the beat, hips, torso and breasts undulating in a slow, jerky rhythm.

Laughter bubbled inside Chiodo and spilled over. He had a vision—God, the absurdity of it: What if they all took off their clothes? What if everybody in the place took off their clothes, including him and Blake, and there they stood, Chiodo and Blake, wearing nothing but their guns and shields, and Blake with that damned radio!

KNOCK IT OFF.

"Man, what I wouldn't give to ball that."

Blake's hoarse whisper brought him back. Chiodo fought against the smoke. He got to his feet, glided to the kitchen, found the sink and splashed cold water into his face. His face was numb. Thirst overwhelmed him again, and he drank water from his cupped hand. On the sideboard sat a plastic dishpan full of popcorn. Hungry! He wolfed down popcorn. Above the sink a dirty window looked out onto a courtyard. He stood there, staring at the window. Time hung suspended. Submerged in sound and flashing colors, he stared at the window.

His mind groped for the wording from a textbook he had read. "Much of the effect of marijuana is psychological." He wondered if the author had ever smoked grass, and fought down another desire to giggle. After a while his thoughts began to clear.

Chiodo walked back into the living room. Blake had left his place on the floor and was dancing with the naked Susie. To a clearer mind the possibilities were no longer laughable. What if the damn fool's gun fell out of its holster? He sat down and watched Blake finish his dance. Then Blake came back, out of breath. "That Susie, wow!"

"Get that stuff out of your head," Chiodo said.

Blake's eyes followed the girl as she moved around the room. It was the old aroused Little Tom, and Chiodo was troubled.

"Look, you get horny over that chick and we'll blow the whole thing, T.B. It's time to get out."

"No," Blake said absently, "let's hang in a while."

"Tom, let's go."

Chiodo's voice had a cutting edge. Blake's eyes shifted to him. "Well," he said, "okay."

A nude young man stood up in the middle of the room. "Hey, everybody, dig it. Susie's gonna do her thing. Sit down. Let's all sit down and groove on it, man."

Someone changed the record. Muted tom-toms began a slow, sensuous beat from the stereo. A trumpet lay down a thin stream of sound. Susie stood with her legs apart, catching the beat. The light from a single lamp spilled over her body. The crowd grew silent.

Tiny movements began in her hips, tugging at her stomach muscles. Gently, her hands lifted, then descended down past the creamy oval face and its tumbling mass of auburn hair, the smooth neck, the firm swell of bosom . . .

Chiodo found himself pulled into the spell of it. Blake was right, of course. She was a stunning piece. The hands seemed to catch hold of his senses. Louder came the throb of tom-toms,

97

while the brass grew richer and the rhythm added urgency. The hands and fingers slipped down, down. Time stopped. The beat caught hold of her, rocking her hips and thighs with mounting intensity. Wilder flew the rhythms, more demanding the beat; and like an opening flower, Susie was becoming exposed. Then she was flinging her head, moaning, leaping, gyrating. With a cry, she sprang to a brass floor lamp, mounted it like a wooden horse and let fly her last reserves in a grinding frenzy, screaming into a crescendo of brass and drums, until . . .

It stopped.

In the devastating silence only her panting breath was left. The long stem of the lamp was wet. She let it fall and slowly, as in a trance, slumped to the floor. From somewhere in the room Chiodo heard a male bellow. Bare feet pounded past him, and then a shaggy-haired man was on top of Susie, back muscles bunched, thrusting.

The act unleashed a spontaneous orgy in the room. Around Chiodo and Blake couples writhed on the floor. Through the laughter and shouts of pleasure, Chiodo heard his partner's voice. "Dammit, Chi, I can just take so much. I want that Susie." But something else caught Chiodo's eye—activity at one of the bedroom doors. Several people had gone in and then come out holding their arms. He put a restraining hand on Blake's shoulder.

"Cool it, man, we've got something here."

Steve joined them. He did not look happy. "Hey, man," the hippie said, "this is turning into a bad scene."

"What's bad, man. Don't you dig balling?"

"That ain't what I mean." Steve motioned toward the bedroom. "A couple of heads in there are making with the hard stuff. You guys ain't on that shit, are you?"

"What kind of hard stuff?"

"Powder, man. They're messing with powder. This place is loaded with smack."

"What are they doing? Just turning themselves on?"

98

"Naw. They want to turn everybody on."

"You gonna try it?"

"Fuck you, man. I don't mess with that shit." Steve wandered away.

Blake was now alert. The partners moved to a tiny vestibule to talk.

"What do you think? Should we leave, get an assist and come back? Or should we take the joint now?"

Another girl came out of the bedroom, holding her arm and swaying as she walked.

"Let's take them," Chiodo said.

"Okay, you hit the bedroom, and I'll take this room."

"All right."

Chiodo stepped quickly to the bedroom door, nodded to Blake and threw it open. Three men and a girl looked up in surprise. A tourniquet was wrapped around the girl's arm, and one of the men held a loaded syringe. "Don't anybody move," Chiodo said. The .38 froze them.

Behind him, pandemonium erupted. Women screamed. The door flew open and bare feet pounded down the stairs. He heard two flat reports from Blake's revolver. Plaster showered down from a wall. "All right, nobody move!" Blake shouted. "Don't nobody make a move!"

Nude men and women sprawled about the room in stunned silence. Blake moved to the record player and shut it off. The silence was oppressive. The partners waited, expecting to hear Banion running up the steps. There was no sound from the hall. Blake moved to Chiodo. "What the fuck do we do now?" Neither thought of the radio on Blake's belt.

"Put 'em against the wall, stupid."

"All right, everybody against the wall. Spread 'em. Spread 'em. Up against the wall."

Chiodo brought the four out of the bedroom and lined them up with the others. The prisoners were crowded hip-to-hip, nude backsides intermingled with the clothed. Outside, sirens were screaming down Seventh Street. Heavy feet came thudding up the stairs.

"Drop 'em. Drop the guns," roared a voice from the hallway.

"We're on the job," said Chiodo. "TPF."

"I said drop 'em."

Chiodo winced as his shiny blue pistol clattered to the floor. "Every fucking time," he groaned, "we go through this."

"Shut your hairy face." A hand rummaged in his back pocket.

"No, dammit. In my sock. The shield's in my right sock."

Slowly, he reached down and pulled the badge from its hiding place in the sock. The patrolman grunted. "What the hell's going on here? We got a ten-thirteen on the call box from your partner. He's downstairs holding three bare-assed prisoners."

Chiodo gave a brief explanation.

Uniformed policemen poured into the room, ogling the naked women.

"Sarge, what do we do? We can't take 'em out like this."

"Tell them to put their damn clothes on."

"Oh. Sure, sarge. All right, put your clothes on. Everybody get dressed."

The wagons hauled 18 people to the station house, plus a quarter of a pound of heroin and a large supply of marijuana, both bulk and rolled into cigarettes. At the station Blake pulled Chiodo aside. "What are we booking them for?"

"Possession of heroin."

"All eighteen of them?"

"Yeah, all eighteen."

"Hey, not my chick."

"Which chick?"

"Susie."

"Sure. It was her pad. And how'd she get to be your chick?"

Blake, downcast, went to talk to Susie. Suddenly the beautiful, brown-eyed girl radiated virtue. She put her head on Blake's shoulder and wept. "Give me a break," Chiodo heard her murmur. "I'm only into grass. I didn't know about that other stuff.

Honestly, I wouldn't have let them in. You understand, don't you?" The eyes gazed at Blake, wet and warm. Chiodo's partner came back, looking glum.

"Let's give her a break, Chi. She's a nice chick."

"Nice chick my ass. She's a slut."

Blake's eyes flashed. "I tell you the chick's okay. She didn't know what she was doing. It wasn't even her pad."

"How do you know that, Romeo?"

"She told me."

Chiodo pulled a note from his pocket. "Look, what's that apartment number? Two-B, right? Here's the communication. That's the chick's apartment, and she was running a shooting gallery there."

Blake studied the anonymously written note that had arrived at the TPF room ten days before. His expression changed. "You're right," he said. "Lying bitch. I'm gonna kick her ass. I'm gonna rip her fucking lung out."

Three times more, Blake made the trip from Chiodo to Susie, from Susie to Chiodo, from Chiodo to Susie. At last, she was booked and taken away to be locked up for the night. The partners walked out of the precinct station in silence.

"Look, T.B., don't take it so hard. You can't be messing with a chick like that. Man, she's no good."

"Don't be giving me no damn sermons, Chi. What's a dumb guinea know about love anyhow?"

Banion clapped him on the shoulder. "Get your head on straight, Tom. It's all in a night's work."

"Sure," Blake muttered.

He left them and sauntered away into the night, alone.

7

Fraudulent Friday

Chiodo was restless. It was his day off. There were no classes to attend at City College. Linda had gone shopping, the two girls were at school, the house was quiet. He finished cleaning the .38, inspected the bore, shoved the weapon back into its holster and put away the cleaning kit. The radio weatherman gave his report in a dry monotone. "Cloudy to partly cloudy over New York today with temperatures in the sixties. There's a chance of showers in the late evening, becoming cooler . . ." Chiodo went to the bathroom mirror and inspected his face. The face looked back at him darkly from a two-month growth of whiskers and was framed in long, unkempt tangles of black hair. He had even let the whiskers grow high on his cheekbones, giving him the look of something from an old Lon Chaney movie.

His mother didn't like the image, of course. She had liked it even less these past three weeks, when they had sent him with Blake and Mayhew into the old neighborhood temporarily. Some of his mother's friends had seen them at work on Eldert's Lane and around Liberty Avenue, busting kid junkies and kicking butts. The kids had taken over the grassy park around the Civil War Monument and turned it into a popular gathering place. This bothered the old people who liked to sit on the benches. So a Brooklyn councilman had squawked for cops, and the call had come to the decoy team. "Report to the Seven-five Precinct. We've got a lot of complaints there's junk on Liberty Avenue."

So there they were, Chiodo, Mayhew and Blake, moving in with their ragged disguises to clean up the same neighborhood Chiodo had lived in as a teen-ager and near where he lived now in Queens. He knew the shopkeepers, the bartenders, the grocers, the druggists, everybody. At Nathan's, where they had set up surveillance, the team perched on barstools drinking beer, with a good view of the street.

"I hear you were walking around Liberty Avenue with a couple of your police friends last night," his mother had said one day.

"That's right."

"Are you working here now?"

"Just temporarily."

"What have they got you working over here for?"

"Because that's where they need us."

"Why don't you tell them no. Don't they know you live around this neighborhood? What if you lock up one of those kids and they throw a rock through my window? What if they try to get your sister because they can't get you? She's only fifteen."

"Those aren't Fran's friends, are they?"

"No. I don't let her go there."

"Okay, then quit worrying."

Fuss, fuss, fuss. But in two weeks they had made ten arrests, and the kids were going elsewhere.

"How much longer are you going to be working here?"

"As long as they need us."

"I would rather they sent you somewhere else. I wish you would tell them to move you somewhere else."

"Okay, mom. Okay."

Blake wanted bigger game than kids. Blake wanted the local pusher. He knew there was a pusher, there had to be one. And then, on the evening the two men, one white and one black, turned up in the neighborhood, he figured that they had to be bad.

Chiodo, Mayhew and Blake were sitting in Nathan's, watching the street. Across the street stood a police call box. One of the two newcomers ambled over to the call box, looking around furtively, opened it, closed it and walked away.

"That's the stash," Blake muttered. "Yeah, I'll bet that's the stash. Let's give 'em a toss."

"Aw, Tom, how do you know? Let's be cool in this neighborhood, huh? No rough stuff."

"All right, then you stay here, Chi, and me and Pat will go outside and give 'em a toss."

"Look, Tommy, I've got a feeling those guys are on the job."

"Hah!" Blake snorted. "Those guys ain't on the job. Man, can't you tell a cop when you see one?"

"I've just got a feeling—"

"The call box is where they're keeping the shit. That box hasn't worked in years. You stay here. Me and Pat'll take 'em.

Chiodo shrugged. "Okay. You toss 'em, I'll watch."

Liberty Avenue was a street of stores and second-floor apartments with recessed entrances. As the two men idled on the other side of the street, Blake and Mayhew moved in swiftly, shoved them into one of the recesses and started talking. Chiodo saw Mayhew level his pistol at the white man. Billfolds were pulled. More conversation. Then the two partners walked back toward Nathan's, slowly. Behind them the two men were laughing. Blake's face was grim as he sat down beside Chiodo.

"Well?"

"Well what?"

"What happened, man? Tell me about the big bust."

"They're on the job," muttered Mayhew, glaring at Blake. "They're local precinct men."

Chiodo smirked. "I wouldn't be too sure, T.B. Maybe they

104

stole the shields. Did you check 'em out good? I'll bet they stole the shields, T.B.—"

"Get off my ass."

"Yeah, that's it. They stole the shields, faked the I.D. What better front? They're out here pushing shit with the best cover in the world. Go back and get 'em, Tom. Haul their asses into the station house. Tell them they can't fool you."

"How would you like a bust in the chops?"

They were pulled out of the neighborhood after that. And now it was Friday, his day off. A whole damn day on his hands.

Hello, Friday. What will we do together, Friday? Shall we study Psychology 202? Turn somersaults? Make faces in the bathroom mirror? Go out and run red lights? Call Freddie? Let's call Freddie. Go pick up the new glasses in Brooklyn, then take a spin out to the airport and see some of the guys. To the phone, then.

"Freddie, Dan . . ."

There were not many civilian friends left, but somehow Freddie had stuck. They had grown up together, and Freddie was one of those happy-go-lucky types who wore well, a handsome Italian with gray eyes and blond hair. To Freddie a job was a job. His job was on a sanitation truck at night, your job was to be a cop. So what? When Chiodo worked at the airport he had gotten jobs there for other mutual friends, and some of them had worked their way up and done well.

"I'm going bananas around here, Freddie. It's like a tomb. Let's take a ride. I've got to pick up some glasses, and then how about you and me going to the airport, see some of the guys?"

Freddie was waiting in front of his house a block away. They drove leisurely to the optician's, made the stop and then started back on King's Highway. The noon traffic was light.

"Dan, you wanna borrow my lawn mower?" Freddie was saying.

"For what? Grass ain't growing now. It's October, man. October twentieth, to be exact."

"I don't mean for the grass. I mean to shave with."

Dan's beard was a constant offense to Freddie's passion for neatness.

"Eight million people in the city of New York and I gotta spend my Friday with the Bob Hope of the sanitation department."

"Work on a garbage truck and, man, you've gotta have a sense of humor."

A new Buick pulled onto the highway in front of them. Instinctively Chiodo made mental notes. Executive-type sedan, four-door, regular plates, no rental. Young black guy driving, medium Afro, big-handled comb stuck in the hair, pullover shirt. The car and driver seemed oddly mismatched.

"Hey," Chiodo said, "that's a stolen car."

"What do you mean? I don't see no sign that says, 'This is a stolen car.' That's some hoople goin' to pick up his girl."

"I've just got a hunch."

Freddie grimaced. "Don't get me mixed up in no cop shit, Dan. Let's go to the airport. You're off. You don't see me pickin' up garbage in the street on my day off."

"Sure. I'm not going to get involved. This is my day off. Screw it."

But Chiodo stayed behind the Buick.

"Wait a minute, I just happened to think," he said. "I need one more GLA for a medal. If that really is a GLA, I can use it."

"What's a GLA? And what medal?"

"Uh, grand larceny auto. Excellent Police Duty medal."

The Buick made a right turn off King's Highway, moving slowly with the traffic. Chiodo followed.

"You gonna screw around with this guy?" Freddie said.

"Probably not. It's probably not a stolen car, but I've got to find out. It's bugging me."

At a stoplight the Buick pulled up behind a truck. Chiodo swung his Chevy to the curb and stopped. He was on the passenger side of the Buick. "I'm going to check him out, Freddie. Now listen. If I give you a hand signal, like this, run out and find a call box, call the precinct and tell them to send an assist. Off-duty patrolman with an arrest, needs assist. Got that?"

"All right, but fuck this," Freddie said nervously. "Let's get out of here. Don't fool around."

"Just remember what I told you."

Chiodo stepped into the street and walked around to the driver's side of the Buick, right hand resting on the butt of the pistol holstered beneath his loose-fitting sport shirt. Instead of having a key in the ignition, two wires hung out of a gaping hole where the key should have been. Chiodo's shield was in his hand. "Police," he said. "Get out of the car."

Gears screeched as the driver tried to shift into reverse but missed. The .38 leaped from its holster. "You move and I'll blow your fucking brains out. Don't move!"

"Man, I didn't do nothing."

Chiodo reached over him and snatched the wires from the ignition. Two alligator clips fell out. The light had changed, and cars were honking behind them. Chiodo ordered his man out of the car and put him to the wall of a building, propped against his outstretched hands. "Freddie, make that call."

"Motherfucking white pig. You messin' with the wrong man, pig."

"Hands behind you, shithead." Chiodo snapped on the cuffs.

Freddie came trotting back. "I made the call, Dan."

They pushed the car out of the street and waited. Finally a radio car came cruising slowly down the street. Chiodo whistled. "Over here."

Two patrolmen got out of the car. One had the young, crew-cut look of a textbook cop, all starched and creased with his buttons buttoned. His glance took in Chiodo's wild hair, scraggly beard and unpressed sport clothes. "What's the trouble, mister?"

"I'm the off-duty cop with a collar."

The eyes widened. "You're an off-duty what?"

"Cop."

"Keep your hands where we can see them." The voice was quiet.

"Hey, I'm on the job. That's the guy I want locked up."

The handcuffed youth snickered.

"Just keep your hands where we can see them. Step back. Easy. Make sure we can see your hands. Now, where's your shield?"

"In my side pocket."

"All right, stand still, take it easy." The patrolman fished out Chiodo's shield. "Now your ID card."

"I don't have an ID card. Never had time to go down and get one."

"Okay. We'll have to cuff you and bring you in."

"Maybe I've got something in my wallet. Let me get my wallet—"

"Wait. Have you got a gun?"

"Yeah."

"Where is it?"

"Over the right hip pocket."

The patrolman eased the .38 from its holster. Behind Chiodo, Freddie laughed.

"What are you laughing about?" said the patrolman.

"He's my buddy. I know he's a cop."

"But I don't know that. Do you know how many shields get stolen each year in the city of New York?"

"Look in the wallet. There ought to be an application for an ID card, a UF201."

The patrolman searched the wallet and found the papers. Satisfied, he handed back the wallet and the gun. "All right, I believe you. You're on the job. But just what kind of job, that's what I want to know."

"TPF, decoy."

"Oh."

Brooklyn's 61st Precinct station was a sparkling new building, in dramatic contrast to the typical dilapidated, smelly headquarters of other city police jurisdictions. It was known as a quiet house with little serious crime, where patrols usually went without incident and detectives grew sleek and lazy. Decoy men were a rarity here. Chiodo introduced himself to the desk lieutenant, who inquired mildly, "Are you going to a masquerade party?"

"Lieutenant, I'm off duty, but I got this GLA—"

"How do you know it's a GLA? You checked?"

"The radio patrolman called it in, but confirmation's not back yet. I'll call NCIC and try to speed it up. I want to get to day court, see. It's my day—"

"Okay, okay."

The call through Criminal Identification confirmed that the car had been stolen five weeks before in Brooklyn. Chiodo took his prisoner upstairs for processing in the detective room. Several detectives were sitting at desks, talking. Chiodo noticed that each of them had a paunch. The heads turned his way.

"Well, well, well, which one's the criminal?"

"He is," said Chiodo.

"Hey, Joe, look at this getup. The beard, wow, four inches of growth. The mustache. The hair falling down. Wow! Looks like a fucking Chief Crazy Horse. Hey, Charlie, come in here a minute."

Charlie came in from the next room.

"Guess which one's the cop?"

"Damned if I know. They both look like skels."

"No, one of 'em's a cop. Pick him out. For sixty-four thousand dollars, pick him out."

"I give up."

"Listen, guys, I'm off duty," Chiodo said. "I want to get this done as soon as possible."

"Will you listen to that? The fucking kid's off duty and he makes an arrest. I don't even make 'em on duty, he makes 'em off duty."

Chiodo grinned. "Look, I can fingerprint this one myself, because maybe you guys have forgotten how."

"Hey, he's funny, too. Long hair, beautiful and funny." The

smiling detective turned to the prisoner. "All right, boy, what have we got you for? Murder? Armed robbery? Junk?"

"GLA," said Chiodo.

"What's that mean?"

"Would you make the fucking prints!"

He could not be sore at them. The detectives were pleasant and obliging. While Chiodo typed out the arrest card and the DD–19 form, the prisoner, John John Washington, age 17, was fingerprinted. The clock on the wall stood at 1:30 P.M.

"Heard a lot about you guys," a detective said, handing him the fingerprint cards. "Never seen a decoy in this precinct though. You guys are real eager, ain't you? I never heard of a GLA off duty before."

"Come to think of it, neither have I. But I like to do things nobody else has done."

"Yeah, well, you get tired of TPF come on down to this precinct." He gave Chiodo a sly wink. "You'll do some more things you never done before."

Chiodo called Linda, who had just arrived home from shopping, and told her that Freddie was bringing the car. "Get dad to follow you and bring it back to the Sixty-first Precinct. I'll need it. Bring my memo book, too."

"Did you have to make an off-duty collar?" She was nettled.

"Tell you about it later. I'm going to make day court and I'll be home about six thirty or seven."

"I've heard that before," she said.

Chiodo went back to the desk lieutenant. "Hey, lou, you got somebody can run these prints over to Criminal Investigation? I don't want to wait for the messenger. I'm trying to make day court."

As he talked, Chiodo calculated the time it would take to get the prints to the Broome Street station, run them into the computer to the National Criminal Identification Center in Washington and get back an FBI yellow sheet on the prisoner, for the court.

"Come on, kid," said the lieutenant, "we ain't got nobody to spare."

"Look, I'm off duty—"

"I said no."

Chiodo stalked back toward the detective office. Sweeping the steps was the precinct "broom," an old-timer no longer eager for street duty and working out retirement doing station-house chores. He wore shiny, rumpled uniform pants and a faded blue shirt with the T-shirt showing at the throat, against regulations. "Hey, kid," said The Broom, "I heard you talking to the lou. Give me the prints. I'll have somebody run 'em over."

"Gee, thanks. That's great."

It was 2:30 when Linda and his father arrived in the cars. She walked into the squad room and tossed him the keys. A detective leered. "Hey, I oughta be in TPF. Look at the assistant you get." Linda gave him a frosty smile.

From the detention cell, Washington was raging again. "Fuck the pigs!"

"Is that the guy?" Linda whispered.

"You'd better get outta here," Chiodo said.

"Let me stay and help you."

"Naw. I'll be home in a little while."

She left.

Well, he would save time now. Instead of calling a wagon for the prisoner, he would take him to the 78th Precinct in his own car. It was a 45-minute ride, and then maybe it wouldn't take too long to get John John Washington photographed and pick up his yellow sheet.

His prisoner was in a sullen mood. "Hello, pig," he said. Chiodo led him, handcuffed, out of the holding cell. "You know who's gonna get your ass, motherfucker? The Panthers gonna get your ass."

"Shut up," Chiodo said.

111

"Panthers gonna cut your white balls off and feed 'em to the chickens—"

"Shut the fuck up."

He shoved the kid into the back of his car and slid into the traffic.

"We gonna burn your house, baby."

Muttering to himself, Chiodo drove to the 78th Precinct station, parked across the street and led his prisoner inside. The place was crowded with policemen and prisoners. They waited in a long line for Washington to be photographed, and then Chiodo put him into another cell to wait for the yellow sheet to come back on the fingerprints. The clock crept to 3:30, then to 4:30, and then Chiodo stopped watching it. The wait seemed endless. "Man, this is a pain in the ass. This is my day off—"

"Patrolman Chiodo!"

He hurried to the desk. The clerk was scowling. "Who the hell printed this guy? It came back NG."

"What?"

"No good. Some stupid bastard used the new print ink without using the new paper. Know what happens on that old paper? The print disappears. Just like disappearing ink. Take a look. The scanner wouldn't even read it."

"Balls."

A sign at the foot of the stairs proclaimed the rule of the house. "We Will Not Reprint Prisoners at the 78th Precinct." It was there for good reason. As central receiving point for Brooklyn, prisoner traffic was always heavy. Regular precinct detectives had rebelled at the added burden of redoing someone else's sloppy work. Chiodo eyed the sign, shrugged and climbed the stairs to the detective office. A lone plainclothesman sat in a swivel chair eating an apple.

"Hi," Chiodo said.

The apple waved him to a seat.

"How're you doing?" Chiodo said brightly. "I'm a TPF decoy."

112

The apple crunched. "Great," mumbled the detective, chewing. "I'm Seventy-eighth Squad."

"Yeah, heh, heh. Man, I've heard a lot of great things about this squad. You guys do a great job."

"Man, I do as little as possible. Don't pin no roses on me. What do you need, kid? I know you didn't come up here just to praise the glories of this fucking outfit."

"To tell the truth, I'm looking for a favor. You see, it's my day off . . ."

When Chiodo finally got to the point and asked to reprint his prisoner, shreds of half-chewed apple dribbled down the detective's chin, followed by a long lecture on the hard lot of the detective in the 78th Precinct, the fickle winds of interoffice intrigue, the strange foibles of certain lieutenants, captains and sergeants, and the dumb sons of bitches who didn't know any better than to ask the impossible. But by the time the apple core dropped into the wastebasket, Chiodo was on his way to get the prisoner with the rarest of all blessings a 78th Precinct detective could bestow: permission to reprint.

"This is great!" Chiodo beamed, inspecting the clean new set of prints. "I've been trying like hell to make day court."

"It's twenty-five minutes after six. You just blew day court."

"Okay, then, I'm trying like hell to make night court."

Back to the clerk with the prints. Wait for the yellow sheet.

At last, it arrived. Surprisingly, John John Washington had no prior felony arrests. Chiodo hustled him out of the station toward his car. It was already dark outside. "Gonna shoot your ass, motherfucker," muttered Washington.

"Hey!"

Chiodo turned and looked back. A scowling desk lieutenant stood on the station-house steps. "Come back here with that man."

"Yes, sir." He led Washington back steps. "What's the trouble, lou?"

"Is that man a prisoner?"

113

"Yes, sir."

"Where are you going with him?"

"Going to court."

"Is that a departmental car?"

"That's my car."

"Get your ass inside and wait for a wagon."

"But, lou—"

"Get inside. You TPF guys think you're fuckin' gods. You gotta follow rules like everybody else."

The prisoner laughed. Chiodo clamped his teeth tightly and shoved the youth up the steps.

"Put him in detention till a wagon comes."

"But, lou—"

"Next time you say 'but lou' I'm gonna write you up."

Washington went back into the hold cell. Chiodo waited. A regular paddy-wagon shuttle operated between the precinct station and the Brooklyn Courthouse, but as luck would have it there were none immediately available. Twenty minutes passed before a wagon finally arrived. Chiodo ran down the steps as the driver climbed out.

"Listen, I've got to get a guy to court right away."

"I'm not going to court," said the driver. "Time for my coffee break."

"Man, I'll buy your coffee on the way. I'll buy you a whole pie. Just get me to court."

"What's your hurry?"

Chiodo told him. "My day off . . . got a GLA . . . disappearing ink on the prints . . . the lou . . . wife pissed off . . . night court . . ."

"Sorry, bub. Coffee break."

"Okay, but hurry up. I'll have my man waiting in the wagon."

Chiodo hurried to the detention cell, snapped the cuffs on his prisoner and hustled him down the steps. "White mother-fucker, you'll be sorry for this. Gonna kill your ass dead. . . ." Chiodo gave him a push, and Washington crashed heavily through the sliding door at the front of the van. Friday. Damn all Fridays. He stationed himself beside the sliding door, waiting. There was a metallic bang at the rear of the wagon and the sound of running feet. Chiodo saw his prisoner sprinting clumsily down the street, still handcuffed behind the back.

"Oh, hell!"

In ten strides Chiodo had caught up with him. He grabbed for the cuffs but his hand missed, and slammed into the fugitive's back. Washington smashed to the pavement on his face. Chiodo pulled him up by the arm. "Son of a bitch," snarled the youth. "You done that on purpose!" His face was scraped and bleeding.

Chiodo grabbed the handcuffs with a twisting motion and pushed Washington back toward the station. Now he would have to clean him up. Couldn't go to court bleeding like that. The lieutenant was standing just inside the front door.

"What happened now, patrolman?"

"He fell down, lou."

"Bullshit." The lieutenant turned to Washington. "Did he hit you?"

"Yeah. He hit me."

"He's lying, lou."

"Put him back in detention."

"But I've got to clean him up."

"Okay. Clean him up, then put him back in detention."

At the lavatory, Chiodo wiped his prisoner's face with a damp cloth without removing the handcuffs. "My day off and you've gotta come down King's Highway," he muttered. "Then you give me mouth, threaten my ass and try to make a break for it. You're stupid, man, just plain stupid. My day off—"

"I'm gonna break my chains, motherfucker. You ain't pushing the people around no more when we get through."

"Aw, shut up."

He put Washington back into detention. The lieutenant was waiting. "Did you beat up that kid?"

"Honest, lou, I didn't. I sure felt like giving him a few shots, but I didn't. Believe me, he fell out there."

"If that kid makes a complaint—"

"I know it looks bad, but I'm gonna tell you the truth. I told the wagon driver I wanted to go to court. He said he had to go for coffee. I threw the guy in the wagon and didn't know the back door was open. He jumped out and took off running. I caught up with him, went to grab him, pushed him accidentally and he fell on his face."

"Are you trying to tell me a prisoner got away from you?"

"Well, that's better than what you're trying to tell me."

"You know what happens when a prisoner gets away from—"

"Yeah. Five days suspension."

Ten minutes later a wagon was ready for the ride to court.

It was 8:00 P.M. as Chiodo put Washington in still another detention cell and headed for the complaint room to dictate his complaint for the clerk to type. Each process seemed infuriatingly slow. Chiodo returned to the detention cell, handcuffed Washington and took him downstairs for his prearraignment interview by a probation officer. As they stood in line waiting for a booth the chief interviewer, a brisk, preoccupied man, came out from behind his desk. He walked with quick, small steps. "Why is this man handcuffed?"

Chiodo glowered. "I'll tell you why he's handcuffed. He is cuffed because he has a hard-on for the whole world."

"We don't want prisoners handcuffed in here."

"He's going to stay cuffed."

"We don't interview until you take the cuffs off."

"Man, that's up to you. When I get tired of this shit I'm walking out of here."

"Suit yourself." The chief interviewer walked away.

They found a bench and sat down. Chiodo's temper was becoming badly frayed. He glared, and shuffled his feet. Finally he jumped up, dashed to the interviewer and grabbed him by the shirt collar.

"I want this guy interviewed. I want this guy interviewed. I want this guy INTERVIEWED!"

116

Heads turned. The interviewer twisted free and dashed into a front office shouting, "Sergeant! Sergeant!" He returned with a squat, bullnecked sergeant chewing a dead cigar.

"What's the trouble, kid?" The cigar bobbled.

"Listen, sarge. It's my day off . . . grand larceny auto . . . made arrest at noon, and now it's eight-thirty . . . wife pissed off . . . hassled all day . . . fingerprints . . . missed day court . . ."

"Okay, kid, we'll get it squared away." The sergeant turned to the interviewer. "Look, the kid's been giving the officer a rough time. So what if he's cuffed?"

"We've got strict orders not to interview a cuffed prisoner. If he's that dangerous, he's got to go upstairs and we'll send an interviewer to his cell."

"Sergeant, you know they won't come up there," Chiodo groaned. "I'll still be waiting here tomorrow morning."

The sergeant pondered. The cigar shifted. "Okay, kid, take off the cuffs," the sergeant said.

"Is that an order, sergeant?"

"That's an order."

Chiodo unlocked the cuffs. Washington winced, rubbing his wrists. "Oh, my hands hurt." Quietly he took a seat in the booth and began answering the interviewer's questions. His manner was docile and polite. Some of the replies filtered out to Chiodo. "Yes, sir, my mother has been very sick . . . I thought maybe I could sell the car and get some money to pay the rent." Chiodo ground his teeth. When the interview was completed, Chiodo was handed a printed copy of the questions and answers. He escorted his prisoner carefully out of the room and then slammed him to the wall and jammed the handcuffs back on, hard.

"Now laugh, prick. I ought to mop up this courthouse with you." The sullen defiance again smoldered in Washington's eyes. "You might think you can fool some stupid interviewer, but you can't fool me." Chiodo gave the handcuffs a savage twist and pushed him up the narrow stairs. "Scumbag. At seventeen you've got some kind of head." He rushed him down the hallway to the detention cell for Courtroom 1–A.

A clerk was looking for him. "Patrolman Chiodo? There's a couple of people want to talk to you."

Mr. and Mrs. Caleb Washington were poor but neatly dressed people with worry in their eyes. Chiodo led them outside. "How's your health, Mrs. Washington?" he asked.

"Oh, my health is fine," she replied, puzzled. "Why do you ask?"

"Nothing special. Did you get the rent paid?"

"We pay all of our bills."

Caleb Washington was a thin, somber man who wore glasses and had a gold tooth. The handshake he gave Chiodo was hard and strong, calloused by labor. "We've been having a lot of trouble with that boy," he said, "but this is the first time he's ever been arrested. We even moved into a better class of housing project, to get him out of the environment. What do you think, Officer Chiodo?"

Chiodo looked out a dirty window and lit a cigarette. The city squatted out there in the dark, with all its ugliness. Even at night you could sense the dirt, the crowding, the decay. Discouragement settled over him. Here it is again, he thought; you make a good collar, or what seems to be a good collar, and good people suffer. They would suffer more than the boy. And he, Dan Chiodo, was the instrument of it—not the cause, but certainly the instrument. What was the cause? Did anybody really know?

"Officer Chiodo?"

"I wish I knew," he said. "A stolen car is no big deal nowadays, Mr. Washington. But there's more to it than that. If he had just let me lock him up, I could have told the assistant district attorney that I'd caught him in the car but that he was cooperative and did not have a prior felony record. But I'm going to have to tell him more than that. Your son has been insolent, abusive and threatening all afternoon. He's even threatened to have the Black Panthers kill me and burn my house."

118

Caleb Washington shook his head. "That boy, he don't even know any Black Panthers. That's just stuff he reads about."

"He also tried to escape from me this evening, and that in itself is a serious charge."

"Well, we understand you've got to do what you've got to do."

Ten minutes before the night court's closing time, ten o'-clock, the case was called. Chiodo looked across the courtroom and recognized the young legal-aid attorney as an acquaintance who had gone to law school with his cousin. At least, he thought, that was something in the prosecution's favor.

The assistant district attorney was brisk and to the point. "Your Honor, this boy was arrested by the off-duty officer while driving a stolen automobile. Subsequent to that arrest the defendant made numerous threats against the officer's life, called him a white pig, said that the Black Panthers were going to burn his house and at one point even attempted to escape from custody. . . ."

Then the defense attorney stood up. "Your Honor, to begin with I find it hard to believe that these threats were ever made and that the defendant ever attempted to escape. Be that as it may, I think it is the position of this court that the background and environment of the young defendant be taken into account. As Your Honor has so wisely recognized in the past, what might be construed as a crime by a white middle-class youngster enjoying the material and social advantages of life might not be so construed when committed by a young black person growing up in a world of deprivation, and the deed is of a nonviolent nature." The judge, a grayish, somber-faced man, nodded, and polished his spectacles. "I am sure," the public defender went on, "that John John Washington was not fully aware that taking this automobile, if indeed he took it, was a serious crime. I also call the court's attention to the fact that his parents are in this courtroom tonight, and the young man has no prior record."

The gavel banged. "All right," said the judge, "I'm going to

119

set bail at twenty-five dollars and remand the defendant to the custody of his parents. Is that the last one, bailiff?"

Washington left the courtroom with his parents. In the hallway, Chiodo overheard him say, "Momma, don't pay no attention to what that cop said. That's just a bunch of jive he made up. They're taught to do that."

At 10:10 Chiodo started his car for the drive home. At 11:00 he unlocked the front door of the house in Queens. Linda had been dozing in a chair in the living room. She awoke as he walked in. He kissed her on the forehead.

"Know something, babe?" she said.

"What?"

"You really ought to borrow Freddie's lawn mower. Those whiskers of yours are getting pretty thick."

Outside it was starting to rain.

The weatherman had been right.

8

The Scalpel

The place had an intimate warmth. Smoke hung on the air. From the shadows came mixed voices and music. The crowd thickened as shifts changed at the hospital across the street. Nurses, interns, doctors and technicians mingled with easy familiarity. Someone dropped coins in the jukebox and Three Dog Night filled the background. No one seemed to notice the three long-haired men in suits. Chiodo toyed with a scotch on the rocks, making wet rings on the bar. At his elbow Tom Blake stared moodily into his VO and water. Pat Mayhew was having another beer. The big Irishman mopped foam from his mustache. "We should have put on white suits, pretended we were visitors from Bellevue. I feel out of place in this joint."

"Give it time," said Blake. He surveyed the room with a practiced eye. "The night has possibilities."

Outside, the snow piled in day-old drifts. It was December 27, 1969, and the temperature had dropped to 18 degrees. Taxis churned past on snow chains, striking sparks on patches of pavement. The bar windows were etched in frost. Whatever the season, the Scalpel did a brisk business. Low-lit and plush, it was a good place to spend a winter evening, even though Decoy Team Three was out of bounds. At roll call, Sergeant Drackus had been specific on this point. Chiodo smiled, remembering the scene in the TPF room.

"How come you guys have suits on?" Drackus had said. "Tonight's not city time? I hope you've got a chick lined up for kindly, lovable old Joe Drackus."

"Sergeant, you know better than that," Chiodo replied. Then he had put in the request for uptown duty, something vaguely requiring suits and neckties. Drackus was dubious but pliable. In this strange business a man had to be pliable. Besides, no hoodlum in his right mind would be out in weather like this. The sergeant gave them a final verbal thrust.

"What's wrong with the Village? Every time I try to shift you out of the Village you scream. You told me it was the only place you were effective."

Pat Mayhew was uncomfortable. "Yeah, well, that's right, sergeant. But we're looking to get away from the hippie thing tonight." After all, he had added, it was two days after Christmas.

"Okay, I'll give you guys the One-eight Precinct. That's as far uptown as you can go and still be in Manhattan South. But dammit, stay in your borough and stay the hell out of Killy's. That place is becoming a regular decoy clubhouse."

"Where's Killy's?" Chiodo smirked.

So here they were, out of the precinct, out of the police borough and halfway through their second round of drinks. Blake, promising pleasant diversion, had telephoned the hospital for Juanita, a busty brunette who came off duty at nine. It was 9:30 and still no Juanita. For the fifth time, Chiodo's partner glanced at his watch.

"Big operator," grumbled Pat Mayhew.

"Fuck yourself," said Blake.

Chiodo welcomed the break from routine. Lately he had been feeling like a commuter. Drive in from Queens for afternoon class at City College, English and Psychology, then sandwich in an hour at the shooting range, then hurry to the TPF room to change clothes and stand roll call, then hit the street. For three nights they had prowled the Village in an unheated panel van, stood freezing on street corners waiting to be mugged, wandered into back alleys and known addict hangouts. He had even struck out trying for a collar in a West Village homosexual bar. Chiodo had wandered in out of the cold, struck up a conversation with an effeminate-looking man wearing mascara and, when the other did not make an outright proposal, invited him out for a walk. They had walked three blocks, trailed by the shivering Mayhew and Blake. Finally, after a series of suggestive comments, Chiodo announced, "You're under arrest." The man looked shocked.

"You can't arrest me," he said. "I was about to arrest you." He was another undercover policeman.

The winter doldrums even seemed to affect Chiodo's pistol score. This afternoon he had shot a .210, 50 points too low. His concentration was off, and there was something wrong with his trigger squeeze. It was all the fault of this rotten city. He disliked New York in winter even more than he disliked it in summer.

"Guess what they did in Miami today?" Chiodo said.

"What?"

"The broads all went to the beach in their bikinis and got sunburned. Then they went back to their fancy hotel rooms and lay on silk sheets, wishing they had a decoy cop to keep them company."

"You want to go to Miami, Chi?" Mayhew said, sipping beer.

"Yeah."

"Then go to Miami."

"How can I go? This city would fall apart without me."

"Gee, that's right. I almost forgot. You're the Sicilian supercop. The city couldn't function without you. Mayor Lindsay would throw himself off the Brooklyn Bridge."

"Mayhew, do you know what an Irishman calls a seven-course dinner?"

"I don't want to know."

"A six-pack and a potato."

"Chi feels bad because he envies the guys in uniform," Blake said. "Ain't that right, Chi? You miss the blue bag."

The door opened with a blast of cold air. Two young men came in wearing white uniforms beneath their topcoats. They stamped snow from their feet and found a table. Probably hospital resident doctors, Chiodo thought. Blake looked around, bored.

Chiodo twirled his glass, thinking. Why the hell had they come in here anyway? His mood was down. Mayhew studied him. "Hey, goombah," he said. "You ain't your cheery self tonight. What's wrong?"

"Nothing."

Strange how he had gone through stages in this decoy work. He wondered if Mayhew and Blake had experienced similar attitude changes. At first, going into the street in old clothes, he had had misgivings. Could he really hack it? Suddenly there was no uniform for protection, no close supervision by a sergeant. You were fighting on your own terms. Was he really that resourceful?

Chiodo had found himself thinking back to boyhood, winning battles in the street and making a reputation as a tough little guy. But those were kid games, and this was real. Was toughness an illusion? Now he was discovering that it wasn't an illusion. He could handle himself well in the streets. And this was spawning new questions. He was slamming the iron door on people. What if one night he shot someone by mistake and the iron door slammed on him? The line between the protector of the public and the criminal drew thin sometimes. He had talked with Linda about this.

124

"In plainclothes, hell, we're not supervised. Our actions are our own. The decisions—you've got to make your decisions so damn fast that there's no time to think. And sitting back in their offices are all those Monday-morning quarterbacks, waiting to condemn or praise."

"You'll do the right thing, babe," she had said.

But was he doing the right thing? What looked like a good arrest on the street could turn into a bum collar in court. There were so many factors involved, human factors. On the street a man might seem bad, a real animal; then you looked up his record later and discovered that he came from a decent, hard-working family, didn't have a felony on his record, might be going through some crazy stage himself, and you were the instrument of society putting the black mark on him. One day you were a hero, the next day a bum. . . .

"Hey, Chiodo," said Mayhew.

"Aw, hell, I was just thinking about Drackus. He trusts us, and here we cheat on him."

"Go tell it to a priest," said Blake.

"Lay off, Tommy," said Mayhew. "Let's have a good time."

"Naw, T.B.'s right in a way," Chiodo said. "We didn't fool Drackus. He's letting us off because we've had a real good run of collars up to this week. He knows what we're up to."

"If it bugs you," said Blake, "why the fuck do you stay on the job?"

"The money. I like to stay poor. Besides, it provides stimulating daily association with learned colleagues of breeding, culture and discriminating taste."

"Learned what?" said Mayhew.

"My dad asks that same question, Tommy," Chiodo said. "He says, 'How come you wanna be a *sbirro?* You want to work for the city and wear a uniform, get into the sanitation department like me. Your mother is making novenas, hoping you'll get fired.' "

"What's a *sbirro?*"

125

"Cop. But the word's not complimentary. It's nicer than 'pig,' though."

"Your dad doesn't like cops?"

"It's not that so much. He's nervous, says the work's too dangerous nowadays—"

"He's right," said Blake. "Do you realize you could fall off that barstool?"

"Okay, okay. Anyhow, my dad says, 'They're killing twenty cops a year in this city. I want my son to draw his old-age pension.' They catch hell even on the garbage trucks, you know. Go into a neighborhood and some punks start throwing empty beer cans and hassling the garbagemen. The difference is, they can refuse to go back into that neighborhood. My old man says, 'Let 'em choke on garbage.' Cops can't refuse. He visualizes someday a bathtub dropping off a building and landing right on top of his boy."

"I'd like to land on top of that broad over there," said Blake. He eyed a brunette dancing with one of the men.

"Did your dad come over on the boat?" said Mayhew.

"No. My grandfather and grandmother did, on both sides of the family. The famine was driving people out of Sicily, and everybody knew the streets of New York were paved with gold. So my grandparents all came through Ellis Island in 1905 and 1906 and wound up in the Lower East Side. My dad's parents had seven kids and lived in a fifth-floor walkup with no heat, four families on the same floor and one john in the hall. They slept on boards covered with straw. They finally got out of the East Side. It was miserable."

"You can't really blame them for feeling the way they do."

"No, I guess not."

Blake was silent, sipping his drink. The bartender looked questioningly at Chiodo. A nod brought another scotch. From a nearby table a nurse giggled. "Howard, stop that. . . ."

More customers arrived, stamping their feet and blowing on their hands. Three young women in nurse uniforms took a booth in the corner near the bar. Blake nudged Mayhew. "One, two, three," he said.

"Yeah, well, cool it, T.B.," Mayhew said. "We've got to hang loose tonight. Any trouble and Drackus will have us for breakfast."

"Who wants trouble?" Blake said. "I'm a lover."

"You ought to transfer to the vice squad. Pussy posse," Chiodo said.

Mayhew ordered another beer. "Funny thing," he said, "the only guy I know who's as hot to make arrests as you are, Chi—aside from me and Tommy here, of course—is Charlie Ficelli. You and Charlie are always leading the lists."

"Yeah. He's Italian. Us guineas try harder."

"Sometimes I ask myself if all this crap is really worth it," Mayhew said. "What the fuck, we bust our asses to make a good collar, get the guy right, do the paper work, haul him into court, and some judge looks down at the defendant and says, 'You look like a nice fella. I'll set your bond nice and low so you can go home to momma. Just promise me you won't do it again.' And the guy's just beat the shit out of some cripple and stolen his watch."

"Well, I don't think you stop being a cop just because some judges don't do their jobs. There are good judges and bad judges, just like cops," Chiodo said.

Blake left the table and wandered to the jukebox near the corner booth. His quarter brought the machine to life. He stood there, staring at the nurses in the booth. One of the girls, a trim blonde with an upturned nose, gave him a quick smile. Blake sauntered back to the bar.

"Where's Juanita?" Mayhew asked. "It's after ten o'clock."

"Damned if I know. Right now, damned if I care."

At the other end of the bar, two white-clad men glared at Blake. Chiodo nudged his partner. "You're not making yourself popular." Blake waved at the bartender. When his VO arrived he drank it off, straight, and shrugged. "To hell with them," he said. "Let's move in on the booth."

"Take it easy, T.B.," said Chiodo.

"We ought to paint a sign and hang it around this bastard's neck," said Mayhew. " 'At Stud.' "

"Come on, let's go make friends."

"You go make friends," said Mayhew. "We're talking."

"Talking about what?"

"About New York's finest."

"Shit," said Blake.

New York's finest, Chiodo thought. The phrase covered a lot of ground. It included the Pete Slades, who took their petty graft to protect a bar owner, and the Patrolman Windoms, who acted out their insane fantasies from behind the shield, and the Hammonds with their terrors of the night and the Joe Drackuses who were incorruptible and demanded the best of their men. He wondered what percentage of the 28,000 actually did their jobs. Twenty percent? Put those in court half the time and what did you have? A lawless society. Visibility, that was the name of the game. Show a lot of blue suits around town, keep the politicians happy. It was like hiring scarecrows; you put the dummies up on sticks around the cornfield and hoped they would keep the crows away.

Could he blame men who turned sour? A man started out young, doing it by the book, and what did he see every time he went to court? The lawyers making deals, the DA making deals, everybody making deals. John the Limp had been a classic. Guilty as hell and everybody knew it. But the system was so overloaded there was no room for him, and no time. Get the damn case out of the way. So they let him plead guilty to an idiotic lesser charge and he was loose again, peddling smack and thumbing his nose at the system. Turnstile justice was like a French whorehouse. Bang, bang, next! Only it was the public that was getting screwed. Back at the station, meanwhile, were the old hairbaggers with 15, 20 years on the job, taking their little payoffs, looking the other way, telling the young man, "Play it smart, kid. Don't get involved." It had to change. Somewhere, something had gone dreadfully wrong with the system. The system wasn't working the way it was intended—

Blake's voice broke into his thought. "Let's go move in on the booth."

"Take it easy, T.B.," Chiodo said.

Then Blake was on his feet, moving back to the jukebox. The three nurses, the blonde and two brunettes, still sat by themselves. Scraps of laughter floated up from the booth. Blake made several selections on the jukebox. Mayhew smiled.

"I never knew Tom was so keen on music."

"Yeah, T.B. is all class," Chiodo said.

Blake walked to the booth, said something to the blonde and slid in beside her. At the bar, male heads turned. The buzz of talk subsided briefly.

"I've got a feeling," said Mayhew.

"You too?"

"Yeah, I've got a feeling."

"We've got to keep it cool."

"Right."

"Nice, peaceful evening."

"Right."

Blake waved happily from the booth. He was feeling his drinks. The nurses weren't smiling. Chiodo and Mayhew picked up their drinks and slid off their barstools.

Their partner laughed. "Hey, guys, this here's, uh—what's your name, baby?"

"Irene," the tall brunette said coolly.

"Irene," Blake said. "And this here's—"

"Margaret." The second brunette smiled at Chiodo.

"Yeah, Margaret. And this is Little Bit." Blake chucked the blonde playfully under the chin. "Eve, but I just named her Little Bit. Ain't that cute?" His hand dropped to the blonde's knee and she frowned.

Chiodo and Mayhew moved into the booth. "This is Pat and Chi," Blake said with an airy wave. The hand dropped back to the knee. Chiodo gave Margaret an apologetic smile.

"Pat, there, he's in the rubber business," Blake said. "Never uses 'em, just sells 'em. Ain't that right, Pat? Hah, hah, hah."

Margaret stifled a nervous giggle.

"You girls must work at the hospital," Chiodo said.

"Yes. We're nurses." Margaret's voice was soft, her eyes friendly and blue. "Most of these people are hospital staff."

"It seemed like everybody knew each other. We felt a little out of place."

"You get all kinds of medical people in here. Charlie, that's the bartender, used to be a medical student. At least that's what they say. Anyhow, he knows most of the terms. Have you tried the house special? It's called a 'morgue cocktail.' "

Chiodo laughed. "What's in it?"

"An ounce of formaldehyde and a dash of fresh whole blood, over cracked ice."

"Sorry I asked."

"Delicious." The blue eyes crinkled. "Maybe your friend there would like some."

Blake's voice was loud. "So we're talking about what a peaceful place this is, and Chi, there, he just loves peace and quiet. So I says, 'I need a little of that, but not the quiet kind.' Hah, hah. When I looked over and saw you, honey, I knew I'd found just what the doctor ordered. A little bit." The hand caressed the knee. The blonde's eyes flashed. She pushed the hand away. The hand sprang back.

"Do you have a cousin that's an octopus?"

Margaret was talking again. A loud rock number erupted from the jukebox. The "Iron Butterfly" tore chunks from her sentences. ". . . Emergency room, and we're not . . . car wrecks and stabbings on Friday nights, that's the . . . boyfriend is finishing residency . . ." Chiodo smiled and nodded. Beside them, Mayhew and the other brunette were having similar difficulties.

They were halfway through another round of drinks when

130

the argument started. Blake pawed at the blonde. "Who're you trying to kid, honey? You probably screwed every guy on the hospital staff. Do I have to be a doctor to get you to open your legs?"

"Shut your mouth, you filthy bastard."

"Fucking tramp, give a guy the hot eye and then turn it off."

The blonde slapped him hard. Blake slapped her back. "Hey," Chiodo shouted, "cut that out!" Chairs scraped, and feet came pounding toward the table. One of the men in white was glowering down at Blake.

"Who the hell do you think you are? Leave her alone."

"Mind your own fucking business." Blake leaped from the booth. His right fist cracked into the man's face. The white suit went down in a clatter of chairs and breaking glass. Someone screamed. A second white suit rushed at Blake, trying to pin his arms. Chiodo and Mayhew pushed between them as the bartender scurried over. "Cut it out! Stop fighting! No fighting in my place."

Blood poured from the mouth of the man in the white suit. Hands pulled him to his feet and sat him on a chair. Someone brought a wet cloth and ice. He sat in a daze, holding the ice to his mouth. Chiodo and Mayhew wrestled their partner away to a table and pinned his arms.

"Man, you blew it," Chiodo muttered. "Now we're in the soup."

"Son of a bitch," Blake fumed.

"Let's get the hell out of here," Mayhew said.

"Stay cool," Chiodo said.

"Is that all you can say?" sputtered Blake. " 'Stay cool, stay cool.' You sound like a stuck record."

"Sit your ass down and be quiet."

Blake obeyed.

The nurses were helping the injured man into his topcoat. Margaret glared at the bartender. "Somebody ought to call the police."

The bartender put up his hands. "Look, no cops, okay? No

cops. I don't want no trouble in my place. What good's a cop gonna do? It's all over, right?" He gave them a reassuring smile. "No need for cops. Forget it. No more trouble. Live and let live. . . ."

The nurses gathered their things from the booth. Two men guided the injured man to the door, and they all went out with a blast of cold air. The room was uncomfortably quiet. Mayhew spoke to the bartender. "Look, we're sorry about that. Our friend here—"

"No problem," said the bartender. "Forget it."

Mayhew dropped another quarter into the jukebox. At the table Blake relaxed and rubbed his hand.

"That bastard had a hard nose," he said.

"Boy," Chiodo said. "Boy, oh, boy. We're spending a quiet evening out and old Tom starts busting up things. From here on in, do me a favor, will you? Keep it—"

"Yeah, I know. Keep it cool."

"Right."

They stayed another half hour, but the incident had dampened their spirits. Chiodo ordered another scotch, but the drink tasted flat. Most of the other customers were leaving. Blake sulked.

"Let's get the hell out," Chiodo said. "Find some other joint. Let's go to Killy's."

"That sounds great."

Outside, the cold pierced their topcoats. Chiodo turned his collar against the wind. Their shoes crunched in the frozen snow. As they started for the car, Chiodo heard the sounds of a scuffle across the street. Two men were wrestling in the snow.

"Now, what the hell? . . ."

In the light of a streetlamp the men struggled to their feet, throwing punches. Mayhew laughed. "Hey, Tommy, there's a fight across the street. Want in on it?"

"Damn right," he said. "What are they fighting in the street for? Against the law to fight in the street." Blake lurched across the street, waving his arms. "Hey, what's going on here?" He ran into a roundhouse left and went down in a burst of snow.

Chiodo and Mayhew were running then. "All right, break it up. What's this all about?"

A stocky, black-haired man—the one who had knocked Blake down—aimed a right, but Chiodo's fist landed first. The crack of bone on bone sent a dart of pain up his arm, but he pinned his man down with a wristlock.

The second man wore a white suit beneath his topcoat and was breathing hard. "Good, hold him there," he gasped. "I'll call a cop."

"What do you want a cop for?" asked Mayhew.

"This guy tried to steal my car."

Blake struggled to his feet, dusting off snow and shaking his head clear. "We're cops," he said.

The man eyed him doubtfully. "Sure," he said, "and I'm Father Frost."

"We're cops," Chiodo said. "What's your problem?"

Still unconvinced, the man explained. "I'm a doctor. The Maserati across the street is mine. Normally I would have left the hospital before this, but tonight I was delayed. One of the young doctors got into a hassle with some maniacs in the bar there. They hit him in the mouth, cut his lip, and I had to sew him up. Anyhow, when I came out and opened the car door, this guy's feet fell out. He was under the dashboard trying to cross the wires."

Blake jerked the black-haired man to his feet and locked his hands in cuffs. They led him to Mayhew's car and put him in the back seat. As Chiodo started to get in the front, he suddenly remembered. "Hey, we're in the Nineteenth Precinct."

"Oh, hell," said Mayhew. "I forgot."

"This is no good," Chiodo said. The knuckles of his right hand were bleeding. He wrapped the hand in a handkerchief. "We're put of the precinct, out of the borough and just finished a barroom brawl. We've got to get rid of this thing."

133

"What are you guys whispering about?" said the prisoner.

"Shut your face," said Blake.

"Look, Chi, go talk to the doctor."

The doctor sat in his car, waiting to follow them to the station. Chiodo leaned in the driver's window. "Do you really want to press charges, doctor? I mean, it's a lot of red tape. You might get held up until midnight."

"You're damn right I want to press charges."

"We've got to take him to the precinct, make out the arrest cards, get him fingerprinted—"

"I don't care if it takes all night."

Chiodo shrugged and returned to his partners. "He wants to press charges."

"What do we do?"

"Take him to the One-nine house."

"What'll we tell Drackus?"

"I'll think of something."

The 19th Precinct station was a weathered brick building across the street from the Russian Mission. A block away they passed police barricades. A patrolman stopped their car. "Are you people blind? Can't you see the barricades? You can't come through here."

"We're on the job." Chiodo flashed his shield. "Got a collar in the back."

The policeman swung his flashlight to the back seat. It illuminated Blake's mustachioed face, then the suspect's, then swung back to Blake. "Are you guys on narc?"

"We're TPF, decoy."

The patrolman grunted.

"What's going on?" asked Mayhew. "Why the barricades?"

"The beards are picketing the Russian Mission."

"In this cold?"

"Yeah. You'll hit another barricade down the next block."

Mayhew drove slowly through the icy street. At the embassy the car passed a line of grim-faced Jews bearing signs: "Free

Soviet Jewry." Three more patrolmen stopped the car and inspected their shields before they arrived at the station house. There, Chiodo made his call to Sergeant Drackus.

"Okay, sarge, you accused us of not working tonight and here we are with a collar. Attempted grand larceny, auto."

"Here you are where?"

"Well, that's what we've got to explain, sergeant. We're in the One-nine Precinct."

There was a sputtering sound, a moment of ominous silence, then, "All right, Chiodo, you're out of the precinct, out of the division, clear out of the police borough. You'd better have a good story. In fact, you'd better have a great story."

"Sarge, I do. We were following this suspicious-looking character in the Eighteenth Precinct. That's what we had in mind, see. We'd gotten wind of this car thief. Anyhow, we followed him into the One-nine and just stayed on his ass. Then we lost him for a while until we heard yelling on York Avenue in front of Doctors Hospital. We ran over there and he was fighting with this doctor—"

"You're full of shit. You idiots are in big trouble. Chiodo, do you really expect me to swallow that cock-and-bull story?"

"Well, sergeant, if we're in trouble for making a good collar, that's up to you. But not only did we get a good collar, I think I'm injured." Chiodo held the swollen hand up to the phone.

The normally gentle Drackus was swearing. His swearing was precise and eloquent, the result of long and arduous training. Chiodo marveled at the astonishing variety of the sergeant's profanity. It was a thing of passion, profoundly understated at first and then rising to crescendos that made the telephone vibrate. Spent at last, his breath an audible wheeze, Drackus croaked, "And just how the hell am I supposed to explain this to the boss?"

"The same way I explained it to you," Chiodo said.

It was a better collar than he had suspected. The prisoner gave his name as John Berkley. "Give me a break," he whined as Chiodo led him off to a detention cell for the night. "I've never been in trouble before, honest. I swear it." There were even a few tears. But the following day his FBI rap sheet told a different story. Berkley, John, age 24, operated under several aliases and had prior arrests for burglary, possession of burglary tools, assault and battery, receiving stolen property, felonious assault, grand larceny and eluding police.

In court an aunt from New Jersey was waiting with bail money. "He's a good boy, Your Honor," she said, "and he's trying to straighten himself out." Berkley stood before the judge in tears. The judge was moved, and set bond at $150.

Chiodo attempted to argue against the low bond. "Judge, he'll never show up for trial." The judge ignored him. A month later, Berkley jumped bond and failed to appear for trial. A bench warrant was issued. When Chiodo returned to the 18th Precinct a call was waiting from Pete Neil of the FBI.

"Patrolman Chiodo? I understand you've got John Berkley."

"We had him. The judge let him out on $150 bond last month, and he didn't show up for trial today."

"Did you know we had a fugitive warrant out for him at the time of his arrest?"

"No. A corrected yellow sheet came down two weeks later and showed an FBI warrant. That's when I found out."

"The damned city of New York," Neil fumed. "It's bad enough the guy was wanted by the FBI, he was even wanted by your own police department."

"What for?"

"A couple of months ago this guy was involved in a traffic accident. It wasn't his fault. Some other car hit him and took off. His car was pushed into another car, driven by an off-duty cop on his way home from work. So this Berkley, he gives the policeman a sad story. He's got no money, no place to stay, and now his car's all messed up. Starts crying real tears. So the cop takes him home, fixes him a meal, tells him to relax and goes in to take a shower. When he comes out of the shower, Berkley is gone. So is the cop's gun and his wallet. . . ."

Mayhew was waiting at the door of the TPF room. "Hey, Chiodo, you ain't still mad at Tom, are you?"

"No. Why?" Chiodo buttoned up his fatigue jacket.

"Uh, nothing special."

"What's on your mind?"

"Well, Tom was wondering . . ." Mayhew grinned.

"Wondering what?"

"He thought maybe if you didn't want to catch tonight we might go back over to that joint, the Scalpel, and grab some drinks. He'd still like to get into that blonde's drawers."

Mayhew dodged the punch and laughed.

9

The Aliens

They rode the big choppers and walked in leather clothes. Chains chinked from boots, and leather squeaked, and there was about them the smell of sweat, smoke and beer. A group rumbled past in the street, chromed engines and exhausts roaring, gloved fists high on the bars, eyes shielded in dark glasses, mustachios trailing. Even in a world where the uncommon was commonplace, people stared. Chiodo leaned against a parking meter. New York, he thought, can accommodate anything, even the Aliens. Exhaust fumes lay behind the motorcycles. "Maybe," he said aloud, "we could bust 'em for pollution." Mayhew picked his fingernails and eyed the vanishing taillights without comment.

It was cool in the city, a dank, wintry coolness. Days had passed without sunshine, and the unrelenting grayness seeped into Chiodo's bones. A lousy climate to look forward to, with the winter stretching ahead. "The sun's shining in Miami," he said. "I'll bet the motorcycle cops are sweating in their shirtsleeves."

"You don't like it here?" Mayhew said.

"It stinks."

"Yeah, but look at all the glamorous things you can see in New York. You've got Grant's Tomb, the Battery, the West Side, Central Park, Greenwich Village . . ."

"I've never been to Grant's Tomb. In those other places you can get mugged."

"Not anymore. Haven't you heard? Mayor Lindsay has put out decoy units to fight crime. The hoodlums are terrified. There are no more muggings in the city of New York. Well, maybe one now and then."

"Did you hear what happened to Banion last night?"

"What happened to Banion last night?"

"Well, him and Ficelli stopped off for a drink at Jack's. You know the place. The bartender in there, Eddie somebody, has this chick he's been humping for years. Nice-looking chick, name's Marge. Anyhow, she and Eddie had a fight, and she was in the bar with a load on. Really smashed. So Ficelli and Banion are in there, and Marge is saying what a son of a bitch Eddie turned out to be and she wasn't going to have nothing more to do with him. She's lolling all over herself. Well, it's about three A.M., see, and Eddie isn't talking to Marge. Ficelli and Banion are drinking wine—you know how Banion loves his wine—and finally Banion says he's got to go home. Real straight-arrow that one. His old lady worries if he's not home by three. Don't know how he ever got in decoy.

"Anyhow, one of Marge's girl friends is in there and she asks Eddie the bartender to take Marge home. 'Screw her,' Eddie says. 'Let her hitchhike.' The girl friend comes over to Banion and Ficelli and says, 'Hey, you guys live in Brooklyn, don't you?' Ficelli nods, and she says, 'Why don't you drop Marge off. She lives in Brooklyn too.'

"They're all pretty well looped. Marge crawls into the back seat of Ficelli's car, and Banion gets in beside her. Then off they go toward Brooklyn. Ficelli said he wasn't paying much attention to them, but pretty soon he hears the broad saying, 'Eddie, Eddie, I'm sorry, baby.' And Banion, he's saying, 'Hey, cut that out. . . . Lady, stop it.' Real straight-arrow, you know. It gets quiet again, and then Ficelli hears this heavy breathing in the back. He looks in the rearview mirror and doesn't see anything. He says, 'Banion, Banion, you okay?' No answer. Then this broad starts moaning, 'Eddie, Eddie, baby.' And the car starts to rock. 'Banion,' Ficelli says, 'what the fuck's going on?' This muffled voice in the back says, 'Shut up and drive.' Ficelli glances over his shoulder and all he sees is this tangle of knees and Banion's bare butt going up and down. Old straight-arrow's pouring the coal to her in the back seat. Ficelli's telling me about it at roll call this evening. 'Damn car's bouncing up and down so much I could hardly keep it on the road,' he says. . . ."

Mayhew's laughter peeled over the street and flushed a flock of pigeons from the eaves of a tenement. He doubled over the parking meter and wiped his eyes. "Banion couldn't make it to work tonight. He called in sick."

They walked together down the street, hands shoved in pockets, two bewhiskered idlers no more noticeable than tens of thousands of others who passed that way. The Village had put on its evening face, like a tired prostitute. Lights blazed from cafés, art shops and clothing stores; street people hurried along with coat collars turned up. A man stopped to urinate in an alley. A longhaired addict wandered along the curb, humming tunelessly. Mayhew glanced questioningly at Chiodo, who shook his head. "Drackus said we're getting too many drug collars. He wants something else." Across the street a uniformed patrolman was listening to a pale young woman. She seemed upset. The patrolman, who Chiodo knew, shook his head and looked around. Spotting the decoy men, he beckoned. Chiodo detached himself from Mayhew and crossed the street.

"How many times have I told you creeps not to jaywalk across this street!" the patrolman shouted at Chiodo. "I've got half a mind to run you in." Then, quietly, he said to the woman, "Lady, tell this man your problem. He's a police officer. Maybe he can help you." She looked wide-eyed at Chiodo, who took her by the arm and led her away. Behind them, the patrolman was lecturing him again. "That's the last time I'm warning you, buddy."

They turned the corner. Chiodo palmed his shield and showed it to her. "I'm a police officer. I work undercover. What seems to be the problem?"

"Officer, you've got to take me home." She was attractive, with brown hair and eyes and, beneath the sweater and skirt, a good figure. He guessed her age at around 23. "I can't go home alone."

"Why not?"

"They'll kill me. They've threatened to kill me and they'll do it. I told the other policeman, but he said he couldn't leave his post. Please, please believe me. I'm terrified."

"What happened?"

"I can't tell you. They did something awful, but I can't tell you. They said they'd kill me if I told."

"Look, you tell me what this is about and we'll protect you."

"No, I can't. I just can't."

Chiodo shrugged. "Okay." He started to walk away. She grabbed his arm.

"Please," she said.

"Well?"

"It's the Aliens."

"What about them?"

"Well, last night they pulled a train on me."

Chiodo was puzzled. "What's a train?"

"Oh—" She bit her lip. "You'd probably call it a gang-bang. They—they raped me."

"How many guys?"

"Five."

"Are you sure they were the Aliens?"

"Yes, I'm sure."

Chiodo signaled to Mayhew, and they met at the car. The young woman got into the car and told them what had happened. The story came out between embarassed halts and fits of weeping. Chiodo grimly took notes. Her name was Irene Rose Sipp and she had come to New York two weeks before from Akron, Ohio, looking for a job. She wanted to be a model, and a cousin who lived in Manhattan had promised to help her get settled. She found an apartment on Thompson Street in the Village and made friends with a girl who lived nearby. Together they had gone to a drinking spot. As they sat in the bar, a group of five Aliens sauntered in. The other girl knew a couple of them, and the men joined them in their booth. Irene had been nervous at first, but the men were friendly and jovial. Her girl friend soon left to meet someone at another club. Irene decided to stay with the Aliens. They talked and drank some more. Finally, one of the men—he wore a black, western-style hat and a ring in one ear—leaned across the table and said, "My friend here really digs you. He wants to take you to bed, baby."

The conversation stopped, and all eyes watched her. Irene shook her head. "No, I'm not that kind of girl." The man with the earring scowled. "Look, he's a friend of mine. He wants to ball you." Irene tried to get out of the booth, but was blocked. Vainly she looked around for help. There was none.

A bearded Alien next to her, wearing a black leather jacket and a Confederate cap, leaned close. "Baby, if you won't let our friend do a number on you, we're all gonna take you."

Irene tried to push free. The man with the earring pulled a gun from his pocket, cocked it and put it to her head. "Where do you live?" She did not reply. "Tell me where you live or I'm going to blow your brains out, right here." She stammered out the address. They forced her outside, put her on a motorcycle in front of the man with the black jacket and roared to the apartment. There, each man raped her by turns. The man in the black jacket laughed crazily as she struggled beneath him.

142

As it continued, a young boy who lived in the neighborhood pushed open the door and watched. Afterward, they ransacked the apartment and found a shotgun in the closet, which her cousin had given her for protection. "All right, baby," said the man with the earring, "if you go to the police, we'll kill you." Then they were gone, clumping down the stairs in their boots. She heard the motorcycle engines explode into life and thunder away.

Irene was sobbing again. Chiodo tried to calm her. "Okay, it's all over now. Take it easy. Take it easy. Is that everything, the whole story?"

"No-no."

"It's not the whole story?"

She blew her nose. "No. I'm so dumb. I can't imagine anybody being so stupid. . . ."

"Go on."

"Well, after they left, it took me a while to get myself together. I was out of my mind. The only thing I could think of was to find my girl friend. Don't ask me why, but that's what I had to do. So I left my apartment and walked over there. It was a place on Sullivan Street. I walked in there and was telling her what had happened when—when two of these same guys came in, the one with the earring and another one. The one with the earring walked over with a smirk on his face and said, 'Well, well, look who's here. I'm ready for a little more.' My girl friend couldn't do anything. She tried to talk to them, but they ignored her. He prodded me in the side with the gun—it was in his pocket—and ordered me out into the alley. When we got out there he pulled the gun and undid his trousers and said— ugh, that filthy man. . . ."

"Go on."

"He said, 'On your knees, whore.' And he pressed the gun to my ear and made me—do—that. . . ." The tears poured again, and she rocked in the back seat of the car, holding her knees. "God, how stupid can somebody be? This place is a jungle. I

143

thought New York would be a glamorous place, full of excitement and opportunity, but it sure isn't that to me. To me it has been a jungle."

They stopped at a café. In the rest room she washed her face and combed her hair. Her eyes were puffy and red when she came out. They bought her a cup of coffee and sat without speaking while she drank it. Chiodo looked down at his hands. His fists were clenched so tightly the knuckles showed white.

"Pat, are you ready to go bust those animals?"

"You're damn right." Mayhew's nostrils were oddly pinched. "Where do we start?"

"That first joint where they got her, on Bleeker Street."

"I don't want to go back there," Irene said. "You're not taking me, are you?"

"You'll be safe, don't worry. We need you to identify them."

"Please—"

"You'll be safe, miss. I promise you."

It was 8:30 when their car pulled to the curb half a block from the bar. The place was seedy and dimly lit, with the atmosphere of an old-fashioned saloon. "Well, I'll be damned," said Mayhew. "It looks like we've hit a gathering of the clan." At least a dozen motorcycles were parked around the club. Mayhew drove the car closer, and Chiodo and the girl got out. She was trembling. He took her arm at the entrance and pushed open the door. Inside, the cyclists and assorted girl friends filled four tables. Hoarse shouts and laughter filled the room. A waitress serving the tables worked through a fog of cigarette smoke. Irene stiffened.

"There's the man with the earring," she whispered, pointing to the back table. "And there's the black-jacket man beside him. And see those men at this front table, with their backs to us? They're the other three."

Quickly they backed out of the bar and Chiodo found a call box. His report to the station house was brief. Within five minutes three radio cars arrived without sirens or lights, bearing six uniformed patrolmen and another decoy man, Frank Stacey.

144

"Hi, Frank, how're you feeling? Looking for some action to-night?"

"Yeah, Chi, let's go."

As the decoy men pinned shields to their shirts, Mayhew offered a plan. "Let's leave the uniformed guys outside with the girl and we'll go in. We're just after the five; the others might not make trouble."

"Okay. Pat and I will make the collars, and, Frank, you be backup man. If it hits the fan, the uniformed guys come in." The others nodded agreement.

Chiodo felt as if he were playing in a low-budget western. The Aliens had moved so that all were now gathered at two tables in the back. As the decoys walked in, badges flashing on their shirts, Chiodo's eye made a quick sweep of the room. The bartender looked up from polishing a glass, lifted his eyebrows but said nothing. A waitress saw the decoy men and stepped behind the bar.

The Aliens and their girl friends, three dour-looking girls in tight jeans and revealing blouses and jackets, lounged over a cluster of beer bottles. One girl carried a whip by a thong at her wrist. Most of the men were in black leather coats, some trimmed with steel studs. One wore a Nazi-style forage cap, and a swastika was emblazoned on the back of his jacket. All were heavily muscled, bearded and tattooed. The man with the ring in his ear had a broad, pockmarked face framed in a tangle of long reddish hair. Maurice Lange, 24, had a long record of robbery, assault, carrying concealed weapons, auto theft and lesser offenses.

Frank Stacey stationed himself near the door as Chiodo and Mayhew approached the group. Lange looked up, his eye flick-ing over Chiodo's badge. There was a scraping of chairs. "Hello, fuzz," Lange said. His black eyes were oddly shaped, flat and slanted.

"We want to question you outside," Chiodo said.

Lange smirked. "What's it all about, man?"

"Come on, outside."

"We ain't moving," Lange said.

Chiodo's hand darted for Lange's jacket, caught a piece of it and pulled. The Alien leader came up out of his chair. A burly, black-garbed figure uncoiled from a booth at Chiodo's right. "Let go of him, pig."

A glancing blow caught Chiodo off balance. He raised his shoulder but the knuckles ripped into the side of his head. Reeling clumsily, Chiodo lost his grip on Lange. Someone threw a chair, and bodies were swarming in on him. Blindly, Chiodo began throwing punches. Beside him, Mayhew gave an enraged bellow and smashed Lange in the face. The Alien leader went down in a wild upheaval of bodies and chairs. Chiodo yanked a blackjack from his back pocket and flailed at heads, hands and shoulders. A figure in a Confederate cap plunged toward him. A stroke of the blackjack wiped away the cap as its owner plowed sideways into a table, buckling the legs with a splintering crash. From the corner of his eye Chiodo saw one of the women leap screaming into the struggling mass wielding an axe handle. He ducked a vicious swing of the handle but caught a glancing blow on the knee. Another of the women lunged at Mayhew, lashing him with the whip. Chiodo spun and saw Frank Stacey step up calmly from the rear and snatch the whip from her grasp.

The door burst open behind Stacey, bringing a rush of blue uniforms. A whistle blasted. The startled Aliens looked up into drawn pistols. Chiodo and Mayhew scrambled free. The room fell silent, and hands began to lift. Boots crunched over the litter of shattered glass as surly, leather-garbed figures moved toward the door. The Confederate cap found its way back onto its owner's head, blood trickling down over his left ear. A cut gaped open over Lange's right eye, and the whip girl was choking and holding her throat where Mayhew had driven the side of his hand into her Adam's apple.

"Call for the wagons," Chiodo said.

A precinct sergeant looked at him in surprise. "Are we taking all twenty? I thought we only wanted five."

"After that brawl, we're taking every fucking one of them."

Chiodo limped outside. The uniformed men were herding the prisoners into line. Lange glared at him. Someone shouted, "Now!" The Aliens made a rush at the blue uniforms. Amid the thuds of fists and gun butts, six of the prisoners broke through and pounded away. Sirens screamed from the opposite direction. With flashing dome lights and screeching tires, patrol cars and paddy wagons filled the street. Two cars roared away in pursuit of the fugitives, but Chiodo knew they were already too late.

"What's the charge on Lange?" said Mayhew.

"Sodomy and possession of a weapon, for starters."

"But he hasn't got the forty-five on him."

"Charge him with it anyhow. I've got to read this cat his rights. Sergeant, you got one of those sheets?"

The sergeant handed him the mimeographed form. As Lange stood in handcuffs, Chiodo began the routine, singsong recital from the form.

"You are hereby advised of your right to remain silent and you do not have to say anything unless you choose to do so. Do you understand? Answer yes or no."

"Yes," Lange mumbled. Chiodo wrote "Yes" on the form.

"Anything you say may be used against you in a court of law. Do you understand? Answer."

"Yes."

"You have the right to have an attorney present with you during any questioning now or in the future. Do you have an attorney?"

Lange gave him the name of a Brooklyn attorney.

"If you cannot afford an attorney the court will appoint one to represent you. Do you understand?"

"Yes."

"If you do not have an attorney presently available you have the right to remain silent until you have an opportunity to consult one. Understand?"

"Yes."

147

"Sign your name here."

Lange signed.

The Aliens and their girl friends, their numbers now reduced to 14, were herded into the wagons and driven to the station house. There, another fistfight erupted as Lange and his friends were being placed in detention cells upstairs. Finally the doors clanged shut and the uniformed men went away.

Accompanied by a precinct detective, Chiodo took Irene back to her apartment, gathered up the soiled sheets as evidence and began knocking on doors in search of the boy who had witnessed the rapes. After two hours they gave up and returned to the station house. Upstairs, detectives were completing the paper work and fingerprinting, and the detention cells were quiet. It was 3:30 A.M. From one of the cells came a small splashing sound. A yellow stream flowed out of the cell along the squad-room floor. A burly detective yanked open the cell door. "All right, who pissed on the floor?"

"I did." The man in the Confederate cap calmly zipped up his fly. The detective threw a punch but missed. The Alien caught him with a roundhouse right. As the detective fell backward, Chiodo and two others charged the door and wrestled the Alien back into his cell. Jeers and whoops erupted from neighboring cubicles.

The FBI yellow sheets on the men recited long criminal records. The man in the Confederate cap, Frank O'Brien, had a dozen prior arrests and had served time for manslaughter, for which he was currently on parole. All five involved in the girl's abduction were charged with kidnap, rape and sodomy. Others were charged with resisting arrest with violence and assaulting police officers. Chiodo also found out the following day that the bartender on Bleeker Street had hidden the stolen shotgun for Lange, but the man refused to be a witness.

"He won't talk," Chiodo said. "He won't even give us the time of day without his lawyer present."

"Can you blame the guy?" Mayhew said.

Their hope for a speedy trial soon began to crumble. With defense attorneys winning repeated postponements, the weeks dragged into two months, then three. Irene, meanwhile, went back to Ohio. The district attorney attempted to go to trial on her sworn statement but failed. "We will have to have the victim in court," the judge ruled. When the case finally did come to trial, the five principal defendants heard the judge fine them $50 each for disorderly conduct.

But Chiodo no longer brooded about such setbacks. For one thing, there was no time for brooding. That evening, as he walked the streets of the Village with Mayhew and Blake, a call came on the portable radio. "Patrolman Chiodo, call Captain Smith."

The cigar-chewing TPF captain was not noted for his patience. As usual, he spoke in short bursts. "Chiodo, gotta special detail only you can handle. Want you to get to the Manhattan Court house as soon as possible. The Puerto Ricans are staging a big demonstration. Something to do with welfare. Understand they're planning some destruction of city property, too. Get over there right away. Mingle with the crowd. Find out—"

"But, captain, I wouldn't do you much good there."

"Right away, Chiodo. Right away."

Blake and Mayhew snickered as they deposited their grumbling partner from the car. A crowd was milling in front of the courthouse. "If they give you any trouble, Chi, shoot 'em a bird. Hah, hah, hah."

Chiodo shouldered into a mob of 500 Puerto Ricans parading in the hallways and spilling out the front door. He remained there for two hours, mingling. Finally Mayhew appeared and waved him outside. "Captain Smith wants you at the station house right away."

Smith was chewing a cigar to bits as Chiodo walked into the office. He spat shreds of tobacco. "Well, what did you find out?"

"Nothing," Chiodo replied.

"Nothing?"

"No, sir, nothing."

"Why not?"

"Well, I mingled like you said, captain, but they were talking Puerto Rican. I don't speak Puerto Rican."

"Hell, I thought you was a spic."

"No, sir."

"Why the hell didn't you tell me? I wouldn't have sent you on the job."

"I tried to tell you, captain, that I wasn't the right—"

"Oh, get the hell out of here and back to your junkies." Chiodo turned to leave. "Chiodo!"

"Sir?"

"Just what the fuck are you anyhow?"

"I'm an American, sir."

The captain ripped the cellophane from another cigar.

10

The Big Carnival

"Chiodo, I've got a special job for you."

Drackus was tired. His face drooped, and there were dark circles under his eyes. The pressure had been on for weeks. The police department had become a social fire brigade, constantly stamping out sparks. Uniformed TPF squads pulled extra duty with eight-hour shifts stretching to ten and twelve, and men could no longer depend on having days off. Columbia was fermenting, the Harlem blacks were restless, Bedford-Stuyvesant was restless, peaceniks were making noise in the Village. Morale sagged.

Happily for Chiodo the decoy units had not been mobilized for uniform duty and Manhattan South teams were left to their regular street work. This was partially due to the attention decoys had been getting in the press. Articles about cops posing as drunks, hippies, women, priests and bums to foil muggers had popular appeal. But it was like pretending to beef up the city's fire protection by painting all the fire hydrants; the decoys

151

were more of a psychological expedient than a decisive force against crime. And while they took some of the heat off City Hall, the wave of disorders and demonstrations put it right back on again. Drackus had urged them to tap informants for word of more trouble. Rumor circulated that decoys might be used for infiltration of protest groups. Chiodo had half expected such an assignment before now, and the idea intrigued him. If he could play a convincing role for drug addicts and pushers, could he also find acceptance inside the radical left?

"We've gotten wind of some new protest activity in the Village," Drackus said. "There's a demonstration tonight in front of the Electric Circus on Saint Marks Place. The inspector wants us to look into it. The leader is a guy who calls himself Redbeard. We've got him as Rushton Cunningham, age twenty-two, white male, goes to Columbia part time, member of the Fair Play for Cuba Committee and several other leftist groups, busted a couple of times for pot, disorderly conduct, things like that. . . ."

"Something messy in the wind?"

"Maybe. What we're worried about is the freaks trying something really bizarre. They're demanding to be allowed to demonstrate without the TPF around, but we've heard whispers that they might try to fire-bomb the Electric Circus. Know the place?"

"Yeah, Hippie night club. Usually packed by eleven o'clock, all kinds of weirdos. Last time I went there my ears buzzed for three days from the music."

"Well, we would like to have somebody inside the demonstration. Mingle with the crowd and try to get next to this Redbeard character. Strictly voluntary, of course, but I figure you would speak the lingo better than the other guys. Banion would stand out like Officer O'Toole, and Charlie Ficelli would wind up trying to collar the whole bunch."

"When is the demonstration?"

"It looks like they're planning a two-day show, possibly three. The first is tomorrow afternoon. If you run into trouble we've got two signals for the uniformed squad to recognize you by. 'The sky is blue' or 'Geronimo.' "

"Okay, sarge. Sounds groovy, man. I can dig it."

"Save that bullshit language for the streets."

Afternoon shadows lengthened over the Village as the crowd gathered in front of the Electric Circus the following day. The core of the demonstration consisted of about 40 males and females, mostly in their late teens and early twenties and dressed in the usual odd costumes. They bore hand-lettered placards displaying peace symbols and slogans. "Stop the War Now," "Down with U.S. Imperialistic Aggression" and "Peace in Vietnam." A small knot of onlookers had gathered, and Chiodo drifted into their midst, blending easily with his ragged bell-bottom jeans, open-toed sandals and a sun-bleached work shirt decorated on the back with a crudely drawn peace symbol. From his neck, on a leather thong, dangled a large wooden cutout of a peace symbol. His hair was caught in a dirty red headband. Completing his outward disguise was the heavy growth of black beard. To prepare himself an inner disguise he had spent half the previous night reading radical pamphlets and intelligence fact sheets. The material yielded little that he did not already know from regular street contacts.

"Remember, now, keep moving. We don't want to be violating city ordinances, so you placard bearers keep moving and stay on the sidewalk." The speaker was a hulking, muscular young man wearing a flat-brimmed Indian hat. He was bare-chested and bare-armed in a sleeveless leather vest. His scuffed corduroy jeans were topped by a broad leather belt with a huge brass buckle. But his most outstanding feature was a shock of shoulder-length red hair and a fiery full beard.

Standing with the spectators was a small, pinch-faced girl in granny glasses, soiled T-shirt and jeans. She smelled of sweat and unwashed hair. Chiodo filled the space beside her.

"What's happening?" he said.

153

"What the hell's it look like?" she said. "A spelling bee?" The thin voice had a raspy edge.

"I mean, can anybody join or is this a private party? If it's against the fucking war, I want to help."

"You'll have to talk to him." She nodded toward Redbeard.

Chiodo waited until the crowd had thickened. Several other bystanders drifted into the line of silent marchers, and finally he joined them. Someone shoved a placard into his hand, stapled to a stick. "Peace Now!" it demanded. Chiodo hoisted his placard and moved with the line. The girl in granny glasses caught his eye and smiled. She looked to be about 21.

A beautiful blonde carrying a guitar stepped from among the spectators and sat down cross-legged on the sidewalk. She strummed a chord and began to sing. "Ain't gonna study war no more, ain't gonna study war no more, ain't gonna study war no more . . ." The marchers took up the song, and their voices rolled over the neighborhood. "Ain't gonna study war no more, ain't gonna study war no more, ain't gonna study . . ." Chiodo joined in lustily on the corner and mouthed the verses he did not know. He raised his clenched fist.

"Right on. Peace now!"

The crowd broke into a chant. "Peace now! Peace now! Peace now!"

After 45 minutes the crowd had swollen to 200 or more. They filled the sidewalk, blocking entrances to the night club, and spilled into the street. Chiodo could see cars coming to a halt as the traffic lane became choked with people. There was a chorus of horns, and a radio patrol car worked its way through traffic and drew up at the curb. Two uniformed patrolmen got out and threaded into the demonstration area. Redbeard met the patrolmen, listened to their instructions and nodded. "All right, people," he said, "we're going to have to clear the street." His voice carried above the singing and shouting. "You people out there in the street, move back onto the sidewalk." The spectators obeyed, pushing slowly back over the curb. The patrolmen returned to their car and went away as the flow of traffic slowly resumed. Chiodo moved over beside the big demonstration leader.

"What'd the pigs have to say?" he asked.

"We've got an agreement with them to keep the street clear," Redbeard replied. He smiled thinly. "They promised not to bring the Gestapo if we do that. I figure this is just the first night. We might as well be nice for now, like we're having a big carnival."

"Fascist bastards," Chiodo muttered. "This is a free country, ain't it?"

Redbeard grunted something and moved away, herding marchers along and clearing people from the path of cars. He worked with swift assurance. Obviously Rushton Cunningham, or whatever his name, was not without experience.

The demonstration lasted another hour. Except for the singing, handclapping and sporadic chants, there were no other incidents. The spectators remained on the sidewalk and, with no outbursts to whet their excitement, soon began drifting away. Only a handful were left, including the girl in the granny glasses. Several long-haired young men finally gathered up the placards and placed them in a neat pile. Chiodo placed his placard on the stack and turned to walk away. Redbeard was standing behind him.

"Not much of a carnival even," Chiodo said.

"There'll be more," Redbeard said.

"Sounds like the pigs have got you by the short hair."

"What do you mean by that?"

Chiodo shrugged. "Nothing."

The girl in the granny glasses joined them. "You meant what you said, didn't you?"

"About what? Doing something, you mean? Damn right I meant what I said. I'm sick of this war, sick of this damned military-industrial establishment and sick of this police state."

"What are you called?" said Redbeard.

"Chi."

"As in Guevara?" The beard split into a smile. Chiodo noticed that the teeth were badly stained.

"Spelling's a little different, but a lot of the thoughts are the same."

Redbeard nodded.

"I'm putting the signs in the van now, Rushton," said a thin, dark-haired youth. Chiodo spotted a slight facial tic and a squint of the eyes. The youth had quick, nervous movements and the face of a ferret. He waited, doglike, for Redbeard to answer.

"Go ahead, Braxton."

"How about the other stuff? Do you want it moved now?"

Redbeard frowned. "I'll tell you when it's to be moved. Get those signs put away." The tone was heavy with rebuke. The ferret shrank, then scurried to the pile of signs.

"I'm thirsty," said the girl in granny glasses. "Are you thirsty?"

"Uh, yeah," Chiodo said. "I guess so."

"There's a bodega still open on the corner. Why don't we get a soft drink. Do you want a soft drink, Rushton?"

"Not now," Redbeard said. The big man was glaring at the back of the ferret, eyes smoldering.

Chiodo and the girl walked to the bodega and pushed open the door. A familiar odor of spices and sausage filled the place. Three Puerto Rican women argued in Spanish in back of the store, something about the price of green peppers. Chiodo paid for two Pepsis from the cooler, and they stood beside the fly-specked display window, drinking. The girl said her name was Shirley and she was a graduate student at NYU. "Sociology," she said. "Minor in psychology. I want to live with the migrant workers."

The face bore no makeup but had smooth, even features, and the hair might have been honey-colored when washed. Chiodo tried to visualize what she would look like with her hair pulled back in a ribbon. He concluded that she might not be half bad, if she only took a bath.

156

"I went to Cuba last year to cut the sugar cane," she said. "It was great, just great. You had the feeling of real comradeship, working in the cane fields like that. You had a feeling of being part of something, know what I mean?"

"Yeah, I know what you mean."

"We even saw Raul Castro. He came out to the cane field and made a speech, standing up in a jeep. Somebody translated into English, but I only caught part of what was said. Anyhow, he was very pleased that we had come and called us brave allies of the Revolution. Wasn't that nice?"

"That was nice."

"Rushton used to be in one of my classes at NYU. That's where we met. I've never seen a man with such revolutionary spirit within himself. Rushton is a revolutionary. They say he got mauled for burning his draft card and that it took six pigs to bring him down." Her eyes glittered. "He's an expert on American weapons in Vietnam, those new antipersonnel pellet bombs and the napalm and all that. His dialogue is fantastic. I've seen him literally slash people to ribbons in debate."

"I've thought about that," Chiodo said.

"What?"

"Burning my draft card, leaving this fucking country, any-thing." Shirley was not too bright, he reasoned, but she was a prattler; he might as well give her something to prattle about to the red-bearded wonder.

"I had a feeling your head was on straight," she said. "I just get this feeling about people. They say I've got ESP. Do you believe people can get thought vibrations from other people?"

"I've been riding a damned college deferment," Chiodo said, "and the stuff I see going on makes me sick. What the hell am I accomplishing? Nothing. Not a thing. Other people are doing something about this war. I look at these guys going under-ground or burning their cards or just plain telling the draft board to go fuck themselves and I think, 'Man, you've got to get with it.' My old man, he's always on my ass to stay in school. 'Make something of yourself,' my old man says. He is being hypocritical, too. He don't want me to go to Vietnam, but he won't admit it. On the surface my old man is one of those country-right-or-wrong guys, know what I mean? Says this country gave opportunity to my grandparents when they came over on the boat and I'm going to appreciate this country if he has to whip my ass. He thinks being a right-thinking American is getting a crew cut and singing the "Star Spangled Banner" with a finger up your ass. I say fuck the fascists running this country, the damned Pentagon warlords committing murder so the arms manufacturers can make a few more billion. . . ." Chiodo finished his Pepsi and brooded into a stalk of bananas.

"Oh, I wish Rushton could hear you say that!" she said. "That's just the way he feels, exactly. Your thinking is so lucid and to the point, it sounds like something right out of a book."

Chiodo choked on the last swallow of Pepsi. She pounded him on the back until he stopped coughing. As he wiped his eyes with a handkerchief, her hand caressed his thigh. The eyes behind the granny glasses had softened. "Are you all right now?" The voice had lost much of its rasp and seemed deeper, throatier. The fingers played with his belt buckle. She was trembling. Chiodo looked down at the fingers and back into the glasses.

"I dig you, Chi. How about us getting to know each other better? How about coming over to my place?"

He shook his head. "I can't."

"Why not?"

"It's like this, babe," he said. "You really turn me on, and if I came over to your place I'd want to ball you—"

"That's groovy."

"—but I've got a dose."

The fingers retreated. She put her empty bottle into a case. "Well, I suppose you will be back tomorrow afternoon?" The voice rasped again.

"Yeah. Same time?"

"Same time. I'll be going now. Rushton is probably ready to leave. Thank you for the drink."

158

He followed her out and watched her walk briskly to a blue van decorated with flowers. Chiodo stepped out of the light of the bodega and waited in a patch of shadow until the van drove past him. He made a mental note of the New Jersey license number and found a pay phone to call Sergeant Drackus. In his report he included the license number, plus Braxton's name and a physical description.

"We'll run a check," Drackus said. "It might take a while. Where will you be?"

"I'll be at Killy's. I need a beer."

"Call back in an hour."

Chiodo drove to Killy's. The place was almost empty. He had two beers, played the pinball machine and called back in 40 minutes. Drackus had just received the information he needed.

"The van is registered to Leonard Braxton, age twenty-three, white male . . ." Chiodo listened to the rest.

"That ought to do it, sarge," he said, "but I'll need a couple of partners for tomorrow afternoon. Backup men."

"Okay, Banion and Ficelli, will they do?"

"Fine."

The next morning, a Saturday, was rainy and cool. At noon the rain stopped, but the sky remained overcast for the rest of the day. At 4:00 P.M., two hours before the demonstration was scheduled to begin, Chiodo, Banion and Ficelli were staked out in the neighborhood. He had already briefed his partners, who took up positions at each end of the block. Chiodo himself hung around in front of the Electric Circus. By six o'clock the crowd was gathering, and the blue van pulled to the curb. Redbeard stepped out. Chiodo searched the crowd for Shirley but did not see her. Redbeard beckoned him over and smiled. "Ready for our big carnival?" Chiodo nodded.

The ferret, Braxton, was busily dragging signs and placards from the van. Chiodo gave him a hand, scanning the interior of the vehicle as he lifted out a stack of signs. He did not find what he was looking for. Redbeard drew a bullhorn from the front seat, slung it over his shoulder and began marshaling protestors into a long, looping line.

This time there was tension in the crowd and many new faces. The placards were openly militant. "Kill the Pigs," "We Don't Want Your Fucking War" and "Fight Imperialism." Redbeard nudged him. "If you still want to burn that draft card, maybe a little later on we'll have something for you to light it with." The eyes were like two pieces of ice, nesting beneath shaggy red brows. "You made an impression on the chick."

"I got better things to do than impress chicks."

Redbeard nodded, lifted the bullhorn and began speaking into it. "Yesterday afternoon we engaged in a peaceful demonstration here at the Electric Circus. We did so in a spirit of nonviolence, with the promise that we would not be harassed or intimidated by the pigs. As citizens we have a right to be here and voice our grievances against a system which is morally corrupt and engages in genocide against helpless, peace-loving men, women and children."

It was a measured, forceful delivery carrying an undertone of leashed power. Chiodo watched the crowd. Redbeard's listeners seemed to drink in every word. The mood was almost ritualistic, as if someone had written a script and everyone but Daniel Chiodo had read it.

". . . It is a system which burns babies with napalm and unleashes the most brutal, sophisticated weapons of warfare the world has ever seen upon simple peasants of a backward country in order to foster the aims of capitalistic materialism. Now we have received reports that even at this moment the Gestapo forces of the TPF are mobilizing against us. The city of New York has broken its pledge. . . ."

The crowd murmured. "Resist aggression," someone shouted. "Kill the pigs!" Demonstrators roared approval, jiggling their placards up and down as they marched. The shouts merged into a steady chant. "Kill the pigs! Kill the pigs! Kill the pigs!" Chiodo felt a chill. Beside him, Redbeard listened to the

160

chants with an expression of grim satisfaction. "We'll show the bastards," Redbeard muttered, "what napalm does to human beings."

"What's cooking, man?" Chiodo said.

Redbeard's mouth made a thin line. "You'll see."

Chiodo looked around for Braxton. The ferret had finished distributing signs and was climbing into the blue van. As the engine coughed to life, Chiodo eased away from Redbeard and shouldered into the crowd. The van pulled away from the curb, and he moved with it, grateful that Braxton was having trouble clearing a path. The beeping horn diverted attention. Hurrying along in the same direction, Chiodo was two paces behind the van as it turned into an alley. He sensed that Braxton would park beside a warehouse at the far end of the alley, a few feet from the exit to the next street. The position was perfect for a fast departure. In gathering darkness Chiodo loped along behind the taillights of the van, moving close to the buildings. Braxton stopped, turned off the lights and climbed out on the driver's side. Chiodo made his rush.

"Police! Don't move."

Braxton uttered a surprised bleat as Chiodo spun him around, grabbed the back of his belt and slammed him against the wall of a warehouse. "Hands on the wall. Hands on the wall. Spread 'em. Get those feet back and lean on the wall!" He was completing his search as the running feet of Ficelli came up behind him. With a savage twist, Chiodo turned his man around and hoisted him up by the shirtfront. "All right, you fuck, where are they?"

"Man, where's what?" The face was green. "I ain't carrying nothing."

"The fire bombs, shithead. Where did you stash the bombs?"

"Man, you're blowing my mind. There ain't no bombs." There was rising hysteria in the voice.

"The fucking bombs you're going to throw into that night club, man. The bombs you're going to roast all those people with, like napalm. Those bombs!"

161

"I don't know what you're talking about."

"Let's kill the son of a bitch, right here," snarled Ficelli.

"No, man, I don't know nothing about bombs."

"Let me have him, Chi . . ."

Braxton's bulging eyes rolled toward Ficelli. Spittle drooled from the corner of his mouth.

"I've got a better way," Chiodo hissed. "Now listen to me, prick, and listen good. You're on probation for sale, I happen to know that. You're also on the needle and I know that, too. Without it, man, you're cold turkey. Cold turkey—"

"No!"

"Besides that, we've got you now for conspiracy to commit arson and probably first-degree murder. Do you know what's going to happen to you, ratface? Your ass is going to rot in jail. Rot, do you dig? Rot!"

"Let me have the son of a bitch," Ficelli growled.

"No, Charlie, not that. The last time made me sick to my stomach. I can't stand to hear a human being scream the way that other guy screamed. You're not going to get your hands on this boy, Charlie. You're a damned animal—"

"Do what?" Braxton's voice was a croaking whisper. "W-what's he going to do to me?"

"You won't stop me, Chi. His ass is mine."

"No, please—"

"Jail, scumbag," Chiodo snarled. "You're going to jail for the rest of your fucking, no-good, miserable life."

"No! Look, I'll—I'll tell you. But I've got to have a break. Promise you'll give me a break."

"Where are they?"

"Please."

Chiodo twisted the shirt collar and buried a knuckle into Braxton's Adam's apple. "Where are they?" The mouth worked frantically. He released the knuckle pressure.

"N-next building. Next building down from the demonstration. That space in between the walls. They're in that space, jammed into a hole between the boards. Bottles of gasoline. But I didn't see 'em there, man. I just heard somebody stashed them last week. Rushton said something about moving the stuff after the demonstration got started good—"

"All right." Chiodo stepped back. "Take him."

"What's the charge?" asked Ficelli.

"How the fuck do I know what's the charge? Felonious mopery, conspiracy to commit vagrancy, anything. Just get his ass out of here and out of sight."

Chiodo grabbed the pocket Motorola from Ficelli and snapped up the antenna. "Decoy One to headquarters . . ."

It was dark as he rounded the corner and returned to the demonstration. He pushed through the crush of spectators and into the protest area as the voice of Redbeard continued its bullhorn harangue.

". . . Listen, I'm going to tell you all about the tactics of confrontation. We are going to be in confrontation right here, right in these streets of New York City, because the whole world is watching. Let me tell you what to expect, those of you who don't know already. You can expect the pigs to come down here in force and start breaking heads. They want to break heads, that's what they're paid for, and that's the mentality you are dealing with. All of you who've been on the campuses and in Chicago know what I mean. You are coming to grips with the fascist imperialists on their ground. Their planes are bombing the peaceful people of North Vietnam. Our brothers are dying this very night in the flames of napalm. Big Brother is in command, man, and he is going to wipe out everything that threatens his insane lust for materialistic oppression. . . ."

"Hell no, we won't go! Hell no, we won't go. . . ."

"Listen to me, listen—"

"One, two, three, four, we don't want your fucking war! One, two, three, four, we don't want your fucking war! One, two, three, four . . ."

"Listen to me. We are against a military-industrial complex

163

that is reaping billions from the weapons of war. That's what has taken hold of this country today, and I say let's give them a taste of their own medicine. We have got to awaken the American people to the fact that they are being screwed and turned into economic slaves by the war masters of the Pentagon. Peace is their enemy! Peace is their enemy! Peace and love are the most powerful forces the world has ever known, not bombs. Brothers! Sisters! Hear me! We are going to make this a demonstration they will never forget. They will not forget because the fires of hell are going to burn here this night. Things are going to be happening here. Listen, when the pigs come they are going to be smashing heads, and I want you to remember what I say. Don't let them fragment us, don't let them take us singly, but in a mass. Together we stand. And when the command goes out, 'Chicks up front!' you know what to do. Chicks up front, and we will throw a psychological buffer into their faces that they can't understand. . . ."

"Hell no, we won't go! Hell no, we won't go! Hell no, we won't go. . . ."

"Remember, a lot of people have sacrificed for us, and we cannot let them down. Brothers! Sisters! Hear me! The jails of America are filling with political prisoners. The exiles of our cause have fled to Canada and Sweden and Spain. Others have chosen prison rather than to serve the capitalist warlords of the Pentagon. Fuck their war!"

Cheers erupted in the street. Youths raised clenched fists and cried, "Right on!" Someone hoisted a Viet Cong battle flag. Someone else raised an American flag painted over with a crude black swastika. Chiodo lifted his own placard and shouted, "Ball for peace!" Long-haired youths, many of them dressed in old army fatigue uniforms and combat boots, jostled one another. The mass of bodies surged back from the street against the building. The mass reeked of armpits, unwashed hair and the pungent odor of marijuana smoke. Some tried to link arms in a human barrier, to clear a path for the placard bearers, but the crowd refused to be moved, and spilled off the sidewalk and into the street. From somewhere he heard a new shout, "The pigs! The pigs!" It grew into a chant, electrifying the mob. Chiodo clenched his fist and led his own immediate group in the chant, "Ball for peace! Ball for peace!"

Over the heads of the crowd he saw the looming green bulk of the TPF bus as it pulled to the curb half a block away. An armored truck, siren screaming, pushed its snout through the crowd at the building next door. Men in coveralls leaped from the truck and converged on the fire-bomb cache. Chiodo felt a surge of relief.

Down the block the doors of the TPF bus snapped open and blue-helmeted men poured out, nightsticks held high. As they quickly formed a line on the opposite side of the street, Chiodo searched for familiar faces but saw none. What was it that Drackus had said earlier in the day? Oh, yes. A Bronx unit had been alerted for possible duty at the Electric Circus instead of the Manhattan troops. Well then, he would see how well they performed.

"Kill the pigs!" someone shouted. "Kill the pigs! Kill the pigs!" But the arrival of disciplined force had a sobering effect on the mob. Few took up the chant, and the shouting trailed off into an ominous quiet.

The traffic jam was quickly cleared. Barricades at both ends of the street soon emptied it of moving cars. Chiodo could hear the quiet commands of the sergeants moving the squad, and the tramp of booted feet. From the crowd the bullhorn came to life again with the voice of Redbeard.

"All right, we are peacefully assembled and we have a right to be here. You sign bearers keep moving, keep moving. The fascist pigs are here to intimidate us, but we will not be intimidated! Any sane human being can recognize their naked display of force for what it is. Keep moving there."

Emboldened, a demonstrator shouted over at the blue ranks. "Yah, yah, don't feed the animals!"

Chiodo pushed his way toward Redbeard. The big radical was streaming sweat. "Good fucking show, Rushton," Chiodo said. He would stay with the man now, ride in his pocket. "But what about the agreement, man? Are we staying on the sidewalk?"

Redbeard was glancing nervously toward the armored truck next door. "Where's Braxton?" he said. "Did you see Braxton? That dirty little shit, he blew it." Then he glared at Chiodo. "Fuck the agreement," he said, and bulled his way toward the street. Chiodo was beside him as he stepped off the curb, shouting, "Tasmanian Pig Fuckers!"

As if waiting for the cue, a sergeant barked, "Get them on the sidewalk. Clear the street. Keep 'em on the sidewalk."

The police line advanced. Redbeard, Chiodo and a few others stood a yard into the street. "All right, back on the sidewalk," growled a beefy, moonfaced cop, his head encased in a helmet. "Get back there." The group stepped back.

"Fucking goons," said Redbeard. "Fucking bunch of goons."

A chant began. "Fuck the pigs! Fuck the pigs!" The crowd picked it up. From their line the grim-faced Bronx cops seemed oblivious to the insults. Their line stopped at the curb, and they stood unblinking behind the sticks. Chiodo glanced down the line. Here and there youthful faces peered out from beneath the helmets. Sprinkled in with the TPF insignias were collars bare of brass, obviously rookies marshaled from the academy. He smiled, remembering his own days of riot duty as a recruit. But he could not feel sorry for them; each man had chosen his own way and was in line because he had volunteered for TPF. Chiodo wanted to walk up to a rookie and say, "Scared, kid? Stomach in knots?" But he did not.

A scuffle broke out beside him. Redbeard had stepped into the street in front of the moonfaced cop. "Get back there, I said." The cop shoved him back to the sidewalk.

"Fascist pig!" Redbeard hissed.

"Shut your fucking mouth," the cop muttered, "and do as you're told."

166

A crew of TV cameramen climbed atop a panel truck behind the police line. Glaring TV lights bathed the scene. The light splashed on police helmets and threw the faces into deep shadow. Marijuana smoke hung in a blue fog over the crowd. The pot smoking gave them an added measure of defiance. Chiodo looked around for other decoy men but saw none. Someone plucked at his sleeve, and Redbeard whispered hoarsely into his ear. "We're gonna bust the line. Pass it along. Bust the line." Chiodo muttered the message to his neighbor. Whispers spread like the rustling of dry leaves. The crowd tensed. In the back, Viet Cong flags waved.

"Down with the fascist pigs!" someone yelled. "Murderers! Murderers!"

The police line tightened. Minutes dragged by. The TV lights flicked off, then on again. "Steady," a sergeant growled.

"Chicks up front!"

The cry triggered a spasm of bodies. The crowd surged forward behind Chiodo, propelling him and Redbeard into the street. The police line bent, and he saw the hippie leader being pushed backward again by a nightstick held chest-high. It was the moonfaced cop. Red hair flying, face contorted with rage, Redbeard lost his balance and went down. From somewhere he snatched up a soft-drink bottle. As he leaped to his feet the bottle arced forward and smashed into the big round face. Glass exploded just beneath the helmet visor, bringing a gush of blood. The police line burst apart in a rush of blue uniforms and flailing nightsticks.

Chiodo went down in a tangle of knees and feet. Hands seized his collar and dragged him to the gutter. Then he was beneath a pile of surging bodies, burying his head in his arms and curling into a ball. His own voice was screaming now. "Geronimo! Geronimo!" Something crashed into the side of his head. A foot smashed him in the buttocks. The other password—what the hell was the other password? "The sky is blue! The damn sky is blue!" More blows. "I'm on the job! Let me up, I'm on the job!"

167

A meaty hand plucked him out of the pile and a fist caught him in the mouth. He felt a tooth give way and grabbed for a blue uniform, to stop the pile-driving fists. "I'm a cop, I tell you—" A blow to the kidney sent the wind rushing out of him. Then he was being dragged feetfirst, his head bouncing off the curb, consciousness fading. The madness around him melted into a blur. The dragging stopped, and helmeted figures were glaring down at him in the TV lights. Somewhere people were shouting and scuffling, but the sound seemed to come from far away.

"Throw this bastard into the radio car. His ass is in." Steel hands flopped him over, and handcuffs ground into his wrists, behind his back. Then he was being dragged to the car, mumbling, "I'm a cop. I'm a cop. I'm a cop."

"You're a bum, a stinking Commie bum." Chiodo felt himself being shoved roughly into the back seat like a bundle of rags. A hand frisked him and stopped at his back pocket.

"Look at this prick. He's even got a gun." The .38 scraped out of its holster, and Chiodo caught the flash of metal from the corner of his eye. He twisted savagely to avoid the blow, but the barrel of the .38 cracked across his forehead. Blood flowed into his right eye. The enraged policeman jumped behind the wheel, and the car lurched into the street. Bolts of pain surged through Chiodo's head. He was screaming at the back of the helmet in the front seat. "You stupid bastard. Stupid dumb son of a bitch. I'm a cop. Geronimo! The sky is blue! I'm a cop, a cop, a cop!"

The radio car squealed to a stop at the 9th Precinct station. Chiodo's captor dragged him out by the handcuffs, leaving a smear of blood on the plastic back seat. Twisting and pushing the handcuffs, the patrolman propelled him up the steps. As they burst through the front door into a blur of lights and faces, a familiar figure swam into focus. Sergeant Joe Drackus stared wide-eyed, his mouth working strangely. "What the fuck are you doing with that man?" Drackus bellowed. "He's one of my men!"

168

"That's what I tried to tell the dumb hump," Chiodo said.

The hand released the handcuffs as if they were suddenly red-hot. "Jeez," the cop whispered, "I didn't know." Keys jangled and one of the cuffs sprang open. "Honest, buddy, I didn't know. I'm sorry, man. I'm really sorry—"

As his hand dropped free, Chiodo spun. His fist smashed full into the man's face, and he felt the crunch of bone. As the cop went down, Chiodo leaped on top of him, both hands locking onto the throat. Shouts erupted around him, and people were tugging at his arms, but he tightened the grip as two eyes bulged from the bloody face beneath him. Then something snapped inside his head, and the lights went out.

He awoke with a throbbing headache, stretched out on a table in the squad room. A policewoman was washing blood from his head and applying a gauze dressing. Blood matted his hair and beard, and he ached all over.

"Chiodo, you damn near killed that Bronx patrolman." It was Joe Drackus's voice. The lean face looked down at him over the policewoman's shoulder. "If you hadn't passed out, in another few seconds—"

"Oh, man," Chiodo groaned. "I mean, I feel real sorry for that bastard, sergeant. I'm screaming the password for dear life and they just kept beating my ass. I feel like somebody's been using me to play kick the can." He managed a halfhearted grin. "Police brutality. For two cents I'd go to the newspapers and expose you fascist pigs."

"Well, I'm real sorry about that password, Chiodo," Drackus said. "We had a little mixup. The Manhattan South unit got diverted over to some other trouble on Avenue D, so they sent the Bronx outfit to the Electric Circus. They didn't know our signals."

Chiodo spent three days in the hospital with a brain concussion and two broken ribs, then was off duty for six weeks of recuperation. In the second week of September he walked back into the TPF room, reporting for roll call. Tommy Blake, Pat

Mayhew, Banion, Ficelli, Stace and the others greeted him noisily.

"Hey, brother, peace. Tell us about the fascist pigs."

"Is it true that the guinea hippies have got a contract out on the whole Bronx TPF?"

"Mr. Chiodo, as an expert on police brutality, would you prefer a nightstick to the head, or a knee in the crotch?"

Chiodo waved airily at his tormentors. "Look, why don't you guys do the city a favor? Go home and play with your rubber ducks."

Sergeant Drackus arrived. "All right, knock off the chatter. We're all happy to welcome Patrolman Chiodo back into our midst, but not on city time. Roll call. Team One, Beard, Jones, Ficelli. I'm putting you guys uptown. We're getting strong-arm complaints again around the park. I want to see some strong-arm collars. Team Two, Banion, Spock, Murphy. You got your assignment. Team Three . . ."

When roll call was finished and they had checked out their radios, Drackus ordered them to silence once more. "I want to say one thing, now that Chiodo's back," he said. "That fire-bomb tip of his saved us from a nasty business. It would have been like a marshmallow roast in that place. I'm sorry we couldn't get credit for all twenty-five collars. But this is the kind of alert police work that makes me proud of you shitheads. I might even get a citation out of this."

"You?" said Blake. "But what about Chi, sarge?"

Drackus grinned. "What the hell does he need a citation for. He gets paid, don't he?"

11

The Pimp

If you make the scene at all, man, make it big. That was Dudley. And here he came, cruising down lower Broadway in the purple Eldorado with the yellow stripes, the leopard-skin top, the TV antenna sprouting from the back, the Continental grill, the two-tone horns. Dudley eased it to the curb and unfolded from the front seat. He was dark, bone-thin, all done up in mirrored glasses, a big apple hat, high-heeled alligator shoes and a white jump suit with red tassles. Making the scene, checking the property, a modern-day shepherd tending his flock. "Hey, Dudley. Hey, baby." They giggled and postured, sleek in the tight, clinging dresses, wafting perfume, catching the tricks and secretly folding the bread into the long, quick fingers of Dudley.

"One of these days I'm going to get that mother." Tommy Blake's eyes smoldered at the Eldorado. It was a brazen car with California plates, $18,000 worth of steel, paint and fabric, and to Tommy it symbolized the man—too bold, too brassy, too unhumbled by law. The Eldorado festered in the mind of the decoy man.

"Okay, Dudley, spread 'em. Time to check you out." Chiodo stared into the mirrored glasses. His nostrils caught the scent of heavy cologne. The glasses were impassive.

"Hey, man, what you motherfuckers want now? You always bustin' my ass."

"Yeah, Dudley, that's right."

"You've got a right to remain silent," droned Blake, "if you can stand the pain."

"Just because you motherfuckers are worth five, six thousand a year and I does a little better, you crowd me. A black man ain't supposed to get ahead in this world."

"Up against the wall and stop flapping your lips, you're creating a breeze."

The search yielded a thin billfold in expensive leather, a big-handled comb, a fingernail clipper and a roll of bills in a rubber band. Chiodo handed them back. At the car Blake and Mayhew yanked up carpet, rummaged under seats, pulled out the back seat, searched the trunk, opened the hood. Nothing. Not even a gun.

"You motherfuckers, this is against the law." Dudley straightened his big apple hat. "You just like to pick on us black people."

"Come on, Dudley, we know you're the big pimp in the neighborhood."

"Man, what's a pimp? I don't even know what a pimp is. I works for a living."

"You're a pimp, that's what you are," snapped Blake. "A nigger pimp."

"Hey, man, watch that talk. You comin' up like garbage."

"We're gonna get you," Blake said. "One of these days, we're going to put you away."

Steaming, Blake watched the Eldorado glide away in a blaze of purple, yellow stripes and chrome. "One of these days . . ."

Chiodo understood his partner's frustration. A year of decoy work had given him a different perspective on prostitution. No longer did he regard it with the naïve tolerance of his youth, a matter of free trade between buyer and seller. Street prostitution in New York was far more complex than that. He saw it now as a vicious network of bondage; legions of hookers working under the command of cold-blooded overseers. Prowling the night in their lavish cars, the pimps conducted a business of fierce competition and held awesome power over their underlings. Purveyors of flesh not only warred with each other over territorial rights, they also were not above murder to keep the women in line. For the teen-age runaway girl, penniless in the city and slipping into hard drugs by the time she was 15, the pimp offered tenuous refuge at best. The free-lance hooker who dared to work the wrong sidewalk risked a beating, disfigurement for life, or worse.

Yet by some quirk of human nature, many of the girls adored their pimps. Perhaps, Chiodo speculated, it was because the overseer brought a kind of order to a chaotic society with an uncertain future. The future of the junkie prostitute was especially dismal. She could look forward to being dead by the age of 30. She also worked at the short end of the economic stick, with few cushions to fall back on. A $15 trick in the Village quickly disintegrated. The room clerk of the cheap hotel took five, the pimp took seven, and the girl was lucky to keep three.

Yet prostitution flourished on a scale that overwhelmed police vice squads. To placate the public an occasional roundup was about the best they could do. One City Hall order for massive arrests in Times Square so overloaded jails and courts that more than half the women were released without trial. Making cases on pimps was extremely difficult, if for no other reason than the reluctance of the girls to talk. The prostitute risked jail rather than betray her connections in the streets— connections that also provided a supply of narcotics.

Dudley, then, was but one part of a vast network, yet a most vexing part. It was his arrogance. Most pimps, when questioned, at least took a subdued tone. The encounter became a little game of wits. "Officer, I know this is part of your job, but I'm clean. My dad lent me a few dollars and that's how I bought me this nice car. It's all I own." Invariably the search would reveal a wad of bills. Where had he gotten all that money? "Well, you see, I got real lucky in a game, man. That's my thing, man, rollin' the bones. I can't get no job because I'm black. . . ."

With Dudley the answers bristled with challenge. "My money ain't none of your fucking business." With each confrontation, Tommy Blake's temperature rose another notch. And the street rumors that Dudley had pistol-whipped the face of one of his girls into a pulp did not help matters.

As they walked, Chiodo chided his partner. "You've got to admit, T.B., old Dudley's enterprising. Remember that night when it rained and we ducked into the diner? Some of Dudley's girls were in there, keeping their feathers dry, remember? What happened?"

Blake laughed. "The son of a bitch came in with a bunch of umbrellas and told them to get their asses back on the street."

As the decoys became preoccupied with other matters, Chiodo could see that thoughts of Dudley the Pimp were being crowded to the back of his partner's mind. But they still burned there, and sooner or later Tommy Blake would have to act.

The months of street work and repeated physical demands were beginning to wear on Chiodo. It was a vague, indefinable thing, which he tried to avoid thinking about. The frequent brushes with violence seemed to be etching into his brain, as acid etches a plate. The brawl with the Aliens, the Electric Circus riot, the repeated tensions of nightly patrols and street arrests, the constant need to be psyched-up and aggressive; each new experience left him a shade more apprehensive of the next one. Somewhere he had read that men in high-risk occupations were prey to ulcers and nervous disorders, and he was beginning to understand why. It was not a question of courage; his courage had been tested and proven. It was a question of how much strain the human system could stand . . .

"What was that radio call?"

174

Pat Mayhew was driving the unmarked car. Chiodo turned up the volume on the portable radio. The call was repeated. "It's down the next block. Burglary in progress. Let's go."

The side door of a men's store stood open, and the alarm was ringing. They drew their pistols to go in. Behind them a precinct car squealed to a stop, and uniformed policemen came out of it.

"Drop the guns!"

The guns of Mayhew and Blake clattered to the pavement as their hands went up. Chiodo raised his hands but held onto his .38. The Smith & Wesson was freshly blued and had a gleaming new stock. That afternoon he had cleaned it with loving care. "We're on the job," he shouted.

"Drop the gun or I'll blow your fucking brains out."

Chiodo dropped his weapon and winced. The new stock cracked as it hit the sidewalk.

After the uniformed men had searched them and inspected their shields, a Polish cop looked at Chiodo and shook his head. "You're crazy. You don't know how close you came to getting your head blown off." The man's hands were shaking. "My finger was tightening on the trigger."

"Yeah, well, that's a special gun you made me ruin."

"Smarten up, kid," said the patrolman. "You can always buy a new gun. You can't buy a new head."

The buffeting took many forms. The game was numbers, and the numbers were infinite. Aggressive police work was supposed to have its own rewards, but the solid street arrest did not always hold up in court. Blending into the street, and yet enforcing laws, Chiodo and his partners often found themselves stepping over the thin line between apprehending criminals and administering street justice. Sometimes street justice seemed more suitable, even if it contributed nothing to their monthly numbers on the arrest sheets. A week seldom passed without some exercise in street justice. There was, for example, the wild pursuit to New Jersey.

It had been cold in the city. Crowds of young people were

lined up, shivering, for tickets to the rock theater on Sixth Street. The battered old Pontiac with its broken taillight sat near the theater with its engine running. Three blacks were in the car. Chiodo spotted the Pontiac on his second pass around the block and stopped on the opposite side of the narrow street. Several teen-agers lingered briefly at the old car, took something from the blacks and went away. "Go check it, Tommy," Mayhew said. Blake got out and started across the street. The driver glanced his way and tramped down on the accelerator. The Pontiac roared away with a shriek of tires.

"Come on! Come on!" Chiodo was yelling. Blake sprinted back across the street. Long-haired youths ran toward them and surrounded the decoy car. As Blake slammed the door Chiodo raced the engine. The crowd in front of him parted. Then they were hurtling up Sixth Street after the single taillight. It was a twisting, rubber-burning ride through traffic and one-way streets. The Pontiac skidded west in the Twenties, through red lights, and vanished. Cursing, Chiodo circled blocks and roared down side streets.

"There he goes!" shouted Blake. A few blocks ahead on Eighth Avenue winked the single taillight, stopping for a light. Chiodo slowed and came up gradually but was spotted again.

"Where the hell's a patrol car?" grumbled Mayhew. "You never find them when you need 'em."

"Hah, that sounds familiar."

"Try the portable, Tommy."

"No good. Static."

"Where the fuck's he going?"

"How the hell do I know? New Jersey plates. Maybe the George Washington Bridge."

They hit the West Side Highway at 90 miles an hour, tires screaming as Chiodo steered into the twisting lanes. A truck emerged from an access ramp. Chiodo swerved wildly to the right, rocking the car onto two wheels and brushing the guardrail. Mayhew's head bounced against the ceiling. "You're

176

crazy!" Mayhew raged. "Fuck him. Let him go. You're gonna get us killed!"

"No," cried Blake. "Let's get his ass, Chi. Get him!"

The single taillight vanished again in the looping approaches to the bridge. "You lost him," fumed Blake. "What a lousy driver. You're no fucking good."

"Great," said Mayhew. "We don't want to chase him over the bridge anyhow."

At the tollbooth Chiodo flashed his shield. The attendant shook his head. "You gotta pay the toll."

"But we're in pursuit."

"You gotta pay the toll."

"Gimme fifty cents, Tommy. You got fifty cents?"

"Fuck the toll. Let's go!"

They went. The long bridge flashed by them. Finally, on the New Jersey side, the lone taillight appeared again. At heart-stopping speed the car skidded into the quiet streets of an Englewood suburb. "We've got him now!" The Pontiac swept into a dead-end street with a shriek of brakes and smashed into a parked car. Chiodo spun his wheel. The Chevy went into a skid, jumped the curb and rocked to a stop in a front yard. As they leaped out in a cloud of dust, the Pontiac's doors opened and three dark forms sprinted away. "I'll take the big guy," shouted Blake. He dashed after the driver.

Chiodo and Mayhew quickly caught their men and brought them, struggling, back to the Pontiac. Both were bleeding from minor cuts. Then Blake returned, hauling a six-foot seven-inch prisoner by the shirt collar. His size dwarfed the decoy man. "You can't lock us up, motherfucker," the man raged. "We're in New Jersey."

"Shut the fuck up," snarled Blake. "We ain't taking you back. We're gonna kill you. We're gonna cut your balls off."

Lights were coming on in nearby houses. Two Englewood police cars arrived, and the policemen jumped out with guns drawn. When the decoys had identified themselves, they debated what to do.

"We'll take 'em back to New York. It's hot pursuit," Chiodo said.

"No, you can't do that," said an Englewood patrolman. "We've got to make a report. We had an accident call on this."

"Don't let 'em take us," screamed one of the prisoners. "They're gonna kill us! That guy said they was gonna kill us."

"What'd you find in the car?"

"About a pound of grass and some rolled cigarettes. They were selling the stuff outside a rock theater on Sixth Street. That's how we got onto them."

The Englewood officers finally agreed to write a report of the car smashup saying the driver had fled. The decoys promised to take the prisoners for a ride and let them out. The Englewood policemen left.

"What are you gonna do with us, Mister Officer. Please don't kill us. Please."

"I don't know . . ." said Chiodo.

"What other kind of junk do you push, fuck?" Blake growled. He smacked the handcuffed big man with his fist. The big man went down. They piled all three into the car and drove a few blocks to an open field.

"What do we do with them?" Mayhew said. "You guys have got to be crazy."

"Get out of the car," Chiodo told the prisoners.

"I ain't gettin' outta this car," said the tall man. "This crazy man's gonna kill me." His eyes rolled toward Blake.

Blake jumped out and dragged the big man with him, kicking and pummeling him. The man was on hands and knees, blood pouring from his face.

"That's enough, T.B.!" An angry Mayhew wrestled Blake away. Then he unlocked the handcuffs and the man hobbled toward a line of trees and vanished. The others hurried after him.

On the fast drive back to the city, Mayhew worried. "You guys have made some dumb moves before, but this one takes the fucking prize. Drackus probably has the whole damn unit out looking for us."

"Don't worry," Chiodo said.

"One thing's for certain," Blake mused.

"What's that?"

"Those three bastards back there aren't going to file a complaint."

He was right. They had not been missed. And no report was ever filed.

To break the tedium they partied. Even with wives and girl friends involved, it was always police parties. At big John Banion's house one night, the champagne flowed, and decoy men whiled away the evening telling stories of the job. Always the talk was the job. It was as if talking about the job relieved its tensions, and champagne and caviar were in order for men who shared the dangers and survived.

The bachelor parties were something else again. A bachelor party was for letting the hair down, blowing off steam. But such affairs, without the restraint of wives, could get out of hand. So it had been at Mike Murphy's bachelor party.

The celebration had started harmlessly enough. Mike Murphy was noted for his sense of fussy propriety about women. For years he had gone with one girl. The off-again, on-again romance was one of those shared jokes of the department. When it was on, the two were inseparable; when it was off, Mike seemed totally disinterested in other women. Finally, they were to be married. Mike's friends decided to send him into wedded bliss with a bachelor party.

"Going to Mike's party?" a TPF man asked Chiodo. "We've got a couple of belly dancers lined up."

"Belly dancers? Man, you should have hired the two broads I heard about the other night," Chiodo said. "They were doing their thing at a party uptown. It was wild. In the big nude act, guys started jumping in from the audience, and it turned into an orgy."

"Hey, that sounds great. Can you get those chicks, Chi? They'd sure as hell beat belly dancers. We could give old Mike a real celebration."

"I'll try."

With a few phone calls Chiodo found the girls' agent. "How about it, Frank?"

"Sure. Cost you three-fifty. I'll set it up. You'll pick 'em up at nine, their apartment. But you've got to promise me they'll get home safe after the show. These chicks don't like doing gigs for cops, but I hear you're all right. They'll do it if I tell 'em. No rough stuff, though. You're responsible."

"Don't worry about it," Chiodo said. But he spoke with an assurance he did not feel.

While Mike Murphy's bachelor party warmed up in the back room of a Brooklyn bar, Chiodo and Mitch Bennett went to pick up the girls. They lived in an expensive apartment building on York Avenue in Manhattan, with wall-to-wall carpeting in the lobby, crystal chandeliers and a doorman. It was nine o'clock. The doorman handed Chiodo a note from the girls: "Back at ten-thirty."

"They're out?"

"They're out."

Bennett and Chiodo waited in a neighborhood bar. Chiodo was not enjoying his drink. Something nagged at his mind.

"What's wrong, Chi?"

"I'm worried."

"What about?"

"You don't know what those bastards are going to do when they get tanked up and horny. Did you hear what happened at that cop party in Staten Island? Somebody was talking about it the other night. They had a couple of belly dancers, just plain belly dancers, for a stag party. While the girls were doing their thing, guys started yelling, 'Take it off. Take it off.' The girls got nervous. This wasn't part of the routine, see. Things got wilder and wilder. They tried to leave the stage, saying the show's over. Then guys were reaching and grabbing. Ripped off their tops and then their bottoms. The girls were screaming and trying to cover themselves. Some guy pulled a gun and started shooting holes in the ceiling. The owner came in yelling and they threw him out; told him to shut up or they'd blow his brains out. The girls got tossed out into the cold, bare-assed. The owner called the local precinct cops. Pretty soon there were sirens everywhere and cops boiling into the joint. A sergeant got up and made a speech about how these guys were going to have to pay for damages. Broken door, bullet holes in the ceiling, broken fixtures. The girls finally got dressed and left with a police escort. I'd hate for Mike's party to end up like that."

Finally it was time. They went back to the apartment house. Mitch was dubious. "What do you want to bet they don't show? And if they do show, they'll be dogs."

"They'll show."

The girl was stunning. She pushed through the front door in a flurry of red hair and green eyes, trailing expensive perfume. Chiodo's eyes took in the trim waist, long legs and full breasts. She spoke hurriedly to the doorman.

"That's her."

"No, man," said Mitch. "They've only got dogs who do these shows. Lesbies. Look like men."

"That's her."

"Five bucks says it ain't."

The girl vanished into the elevator and soon returned with another woman, older, stockier, taller. They walked over to Mitch and Chiodo. "You got my note?" said the redhead.

"Uh-huh."

Mitch grinned. "I lose. But I win too."

"Let's go," Chiodo said.

"Wait a minute, is this on the level?" she said. "Did Frank tell you how much we get paid? I want it now."

"You'll get your bread when we get to the show."

"Bullshit," she said. "We get ripped off by you pigs all the time. No bread, no show."

"That's up to you. Go peddle your ass on the corner."

"Wait a minute." She drew her companion aside, and they talked. The redhead nodded. They came back. "We'll take a chance, but I don't like it."

In the car she and Chiodo argued. The women sat in the back seat, and Mitch and Chiodo in the front. The redhead was needling him. "Pigs," she said. "Always looking for freebies."

He stopped the car and turned in the seat to glare at her. "You use that word one more time, I'll put my foot in your mouth."

"Cool it, Chi," Mitch said. "What are you getting in a fight with this broad for? Let's take 'em where we promised and forget about it."

Chiodo drove the rest of the way in a surly mood, ignoring the conversation in the back.

"Didn't we make a promise once," muttered the redhead, "not to put on shows for horny cops? What about that, Rita?"

"Why don't you shut up," snapped the other woman. "A job's a job. What the hell you care who we do it for?"

The crowd was in a boisterous mood. The tables had been pushed back, leaving an open space in the middle of the room in front of the stage. Cigar smoke filled the air, and men were shouting for more movies. Chiodo saw a screen and a movie projector.

"What the hell's going on?"

"They've been showing smokers," replied Wayne Brightley, the unofficial host. "This crowd's horny as hell. Are these the chicks?" He looked the redhead over and gave a low whistle.

"Yeah. Where do they—uh—dress?"

"In the kitchen."

"We get paid," said the redhead.

182

"Yeah, yeah, you get paid." They pushed through the crowd and into the kitchen. Chiodo closed the door, and Brightley handed over a wad of folded bills. Expertly the redhead flicked through the stack of twenties, tucked them into her purse and peeled off her green blouse, freeing a pair of magnificent breasts. Brightley swallowed hard. Chiodo lit a cigarette. Mitch coughed.

The women undressed quickly and were standing in the nude when someone banged on the door. "Hey, what the hell's goin' on?" shouted drunken voices. "What's holdin' up the party?"

A waitress walked in. She was an Italian woman, about 50. Startled, she glanced at the naked redhead and blushed.

"Oh, hello. Aren't you afraid you'll catch cold, dear?"

"Maria," said Brightley, "this here's—uh—"

"Dawn," said the redhead, smiling.

"Pleased to meet you, I'm sure," said Maria.

"We need a bed sheet for the act. You got a bed sheet or a blanket of some kind to put on the floor?"

"Why, certainly. Are we going to have a picnic?"

The redhead laughed huskily. "Sure, honey, and you can share our basket of goodies."

Maria vanished. There was more banging on the door. A beefy TPF cop pushed through, ogling the girls. "Get the hell out of here, Fred. Come on, move out, you guys."

As the lights went down, the women moved smoothly out onto the floor, their bodies draped in filmy material. Maria fed quarters into the jukebox and a slow rock instrumental came to life. In the murky light, male eyes glistened at the gyrating bodies of the women. The scarves loosened and fell, and the bodies went through fluid pelvic rhythms. Hands played across flesh, and the redhead swooned and wet her lips with her tongue. Then the bodies were swaying together, and men were shouting encouragement to the dancers. "Shake 'em, baby. Get into it. Whooee." The dancers melted down together onto the bedsheet with the older woman on top, touching, stroking.

"Hey, that's it. Go after it. Go after it."

183

"Hey, put that thing away, man."

"I'm gonna get me a piece of that."

"Get out of there, you crazy bastard!"

Chiodo stood in the back of the crowd, nursing a drink. He should have known better, damn it. Should have kept his mouth shut. All these guys riled up. Now there was going to be hell to pay. . . .

The redhead was screeching over the noise. "If you guys don't stay back, we're leaving. One more guy comes jumping in here, we're walking out."

"You ain't walking nowhere, baby. Just get on with the show. Get on with the show."

Chiodo buried his nose in the scotch. Should have left well enough alone. Beside him Maria peered through the crush of men, eyes sparkling. She seemed oddly out of place in her prim waitress uniform with its starched collar and apron tied in a bow. Probably got a houseful of kids, Chiodo thought.

"Who's Mike?" the redhead was saying.

"Here I am." A figure lurched to its feet in the middle of the crowd and moved forward unsteadily through the crush of men.

"Come here, sweetheart," Dawn murmured. "Come over here to me, baby. I'm going to fix you up real good tonight."

Over the silhouetted heads, Chiodo saw the bridegroom's face wreathed in a bemused smile as hands worked deftly at his shirt collar. The shirt flew aside, then a pair of pants, shoes, socks, underwear.

"Hey, get it, Mike," shouted a voice in the crowd. "Put it to her, boy."

Some of the cops were taking bets. "Five bucks says old straight-arrow won't put it in."

"I got ten says he will."

"No way. He won't go for that."

Maria the waitress leaped onto a chair. "Fifteen," she screamed. "Do I hear fifteen dollars for the bridegroom to put it in?"

"Fifteen! I'll pay the son of a bitch fifteen."

"Twenty!"

"Somebody make it fifty!" shouted Maria. "Give that boy a wedding present. Do I hear fifty? Fifty, fifty, fifty?"

"Fifty!"

"Who said fifty?" It was Mike Murphy's voice, strangely muffled but distinct.

"I did."

"Attaboy, Mike. Give it to her, Mike."

"Hey, look at him pour the coal to that bitch."

"Yeah, he just found out what that thing's for."

"Give it to her, Mike!" It was Maria, jumping up and down on the chair.

"Careful, honey," said Chiodo, "you'll fall off."

"No she won't. I'm gonna hold her up." One of the men thrust his hands up her dress and grabbed her by the hips.

Maria giggled. "Quit that!" But she didn't push the hands away.

Men surged up from the tables, pushing forward. "Hold my gun, somebody!" A tall, thin man burst into the arena, unbuckling his belt. Struggling forms and bare buttocks made a weird tableau in the middle of the dance floor.

Someone hammered at the door. "What's going on in there? I don't want this going on in my place. They'll close me down. Cops or no cops, get out. Get out!"

"Stay out of here," someone yelled back through the door. "We'll bust your head!"

"Wait a minute," cried the redhead. "WAIT A MINUTE!"

The shouting stopped.

Someone was struggling behind her, arms locked around her waist. She glanced over her shoulder. "Are you done yet?"

"I c-can't. Just a couple more. Couple more. Couple more. There. . . ."

"Listen," said Rita, disentangling herself from a hairy arm, "we can't take care of all you guys. The deal was we'd just take care of Mike."

But the performance went on. Then the girls were scrambling to their feet, trying to get to the kitchen. "Show's over." But it wasn't. More men surged around them. "All right. One more, just one more."

Finally they made it to the kitchen, pushing past a young cop named Pat who had been waiting patiently and was next in line. Disappointment showed in his face. Chiodo and Brightley formed a rear guard and jammed the door shut. The redhead wiped sweat from her face with a towel. "Jeez, I must have taken care of ten of you horny cops."

Chiodo wagged his head in disgust. "Brightley, bring young Pat in here. We've got to get these broads home." Soon Brightley was pushing his way back into the kitchen, followed by Pat.

"Okay, Pat, you want to take 'em home?"

"Yeah, Chi." His eyes lit up. "I'll be glad to take them home, you bet."

"All right, then, I'm making you responsible. Nothing happens to these chicks; they get back to their apartment safe and sound, okay?"

"Sure, Chi. I'll get them back okay."

The redhead stopped dressing and turned to Chiodo. "The deal is, you take us home," she said. "You brought us here, you take us home."

"I've got something else to do. Besides, the kid wants to get a little. I guess he's not so choosy."

She ignored the remark, walked over to Chiodo and put her hand lightly on his chest. When she spoke again the voice was softly sensuous. The eyes had a melting warmth. "We started out on the wrong foot, and I'm sorry about that. I want you to take me home. I've got something special for you when we get there."

"What's so special?"

"I'm going to give it to you like you've never had it before. Come on, take me home."

Chiodo shook the hand away. "Let me tell you something,

186

sweetheart. If I did go home with you, you'd enjoy it for a change and probably quit being a dyke."

The green eyes flared. "What do you mean? I'm no dyke! Do you think I enjoy doing this stuff with her?"

"You look like you're enjoying it."

"I do it for the bread, that's all. I've been married. I've got three kids."

"Do you live with your old man?"

"No. We're divorced."

"What happened? Did he catch you in bed with your girl friend?"

She cursed, swung at him and missed, picked up a pan and flung it across the kitchen. Chiodo grabbed her hands. "Cool it, baby."

She calmed down again. "I want you to take me home. I'll show you I'm straight."

"Forget it. Let Pat take you home, or take a bus."

Dawn picked up her purse, straightened her blouse and gave him a final icy stare. "Go to hell," she said.

Then, chin high, she marched out of the kitchen.

For men who lived the dangers of the streets, such episodes seemed necessary to break the tension. Parties, broads, booze. Most of their boozing was done at Killy's, a favorite watering place for police. The rule at Killy's was that everyone paid his tab, regardless of precinct, squad or rank. Men loosened in the warmth of Killy's potent mixes. Chiodo and Bob Parr, an ex–Green Beret who owned the place, pushed back tables and engaged in mock karate matches. Sometimes, too, the conflict was verbal, between decoy men and precinct cops out of uniform. One night it was an old-timer from Chinatown's 5th Precinct.

"You TPF guys come into a fucking precinct, raise hell, make a lotta bullshit collars and scram. You don't have to live with them people year after year. We do. It makes a difference."

"Hell, somebody's got to do it. You fucking precinct guys don't know what arrests are. I know a guy retiring after twenty years who made three felony collars in all that time. Three! Man, what kind of police work is that? If that guy saw an armed robbery going on, he'd probably offer to hold the scumbag's coat."

"Now just a damn minute, kid. Before you go badmouthing precinct cops you'd better look back at the guys killed in line of duty. There's some damn fine men in these precincts, and don't you forget it. We've got guys whose fathers, uncles, brothers, cousins and grandfathers were cops. Police work ain't all making numbers, by a long shot. You got people out there that need help, all kinds of help, from delivering babies in the back of an RMP to getting a doctor for a sick old man and breakin' up family squabbles. Why, I remember the time—"

"Yeah, well you got hairbaggers in this department that's been taking payoffs for so long they think it's part of their salary. You put a guy on the polygraph who's been taking for fifteen years and I'll bet he can justify every dime. A pound here, a sawbuck there, a C-note somewhere else. In your own precinct, Chinatown, just add up the free coffee, cigarettes and Mandarin-duck dinners one guy takes in twenty years and you've got a small fortune."

"Let me tell you something, kid. You're young yet. You think you can change the world. You're still a hero, out bustin' your balls for the numbers. But there's still a family to feed, clothe and shelter and kids to send to school. And one of these days, when you turn up dead, you'll be no good to them no more. So your old lady gets a nice letter of commendation to hang on the fucking wall. That won't keep a woman warm on a cold night. If you bust your ass on the job, nobody's gonna give a damn but the people who depend on you, and they'll wish you hadn't."

"All right, then, what do you suggest we do, let the punks and shitheads take over the city? Have a completely lawless society? I heard business is so good in the precincts nowadays that even the bagmen have bagmen."

"You got evidence of that? Take it to the commissioner."

Chiodo came away from such debates deflated and irritable. He did not believe that change was impossible, either in the police department, the courts or society itself. In time it had to come. For now, he was merely a tiny piece of the system. But at least he could help make things uncomfortable for those who clung to the status quo. Even a small amount of discomfort would be something. Maybe he should also try to become a Patrolmen's Benevolent Association delegate. At least it would give him a stronger voice than he had now. Yes, he would have to think about that. . . .

They made an arrest in the early evening. A light drizzle wetted down the streets. By the time they arrived at the Manhattan Courthouse the drizzle had stopped and water was chuckling down the storm drains. Chiodo hoped that Officer Trace was off duty. Officer Trace was a nuisance. On traffic duty in front of the courthouse, he made it his business to see that judges and lawyers got favored parking spaces and shooed away people of lesser importance. But he was there, damn it, standing in his big wet shoes and waving Chiodo away from the parking spot he had wanted. Another car, however, had been permitted to park. It was a purple Eldorado with yellow stripes and a leopard-skin top. "Dudley," muttered Tommy Blake. "How does that scumbag rate?" They found a space in a nearby parking lot.

"Dudley must be bailing out one of his chicks," said Mayhew.

Blake was silent.

"Well, let's go in and get the damn paper work done. Coming, Tom?"

"Naw. I'm going over to Marsh's for a cool one."

"Okay, Pat and I'll get the stuff finished and we'll meet you there."

The business in the courthouse took half an hour. When Chiodo and Mayhew walked out, Tommy Blake was sitting on the hood of the Eldorado across the street. The big car had four flat tires. A huge grin spread across Blake's face. They hurried over to him.

"What'd you do that for?" said Mayhew.

"If I can't get that mother with a collar, at least I got his wheels. Wait till he comes out and sees this. Hah, hah, hah."

"What are you doing sitting on the damn car?"

"I want to see his face."

"Come on, Tom, let's go get a cool one."

"No. I'm gonna sit here till that bastard comes out."

They talked Blake into leaving the Eldorado and waiting in Chiodo's car in the parking lot. "He'll know it's you, Tom. Me and Pat need a beer."

They were finishing their first round when a uniformed TPF man hurried into the bar. "Hey, Tommy's in big trouble," he announced.

"What do you mean he's in trouble?"

"He was beating on a black guy outside the courthouse. Some of the precinct men tried to stop it, and he slugged one of them. He slugged Trace."

"Oh, shit."

The Eldorado still sat on its four flat tires, but there was no Tommy in the street. A uniformed man jerked his thumb toward the courthouse. "He's in the lieutenant's office." Bloodstains spattered the asphalt beside the car.

Tommy sat quietly in a chair beside the lieutenant's desk. The lieutenant was a middle-aged man with a flushed face, thinning red hair and steel-rimmed glasses. His blood pressure was up. As Chiodo and Mayhew walked in, he whirled in his chair. "Are you two working with this guy?"

"Yeah, lou, we're working with him."

"Whadda you leave a maniac like this loose for? You shoulda watched him. It's as much your fault as it is his."

"What happened?"

"What happened? What happened? My God, what didn't happen? This guy starts beating on a pimp in the street. There's

190

judges, reporters, lawyers and everything else swarming around this courthouse, and he starts beating on a pimp. Some of my guys go to pull him off, and he slugs one of 'em with a blackjack."

"No, that didn't happen."

"Yeah, it happened all right," Blake said sullenly. "It happened. It's that fuck that's always chasing us away from the parking space. . . ."

Slowly the incident was pieced together. Dudley had come out of the courthouse with two of his girls. The sight of the flattened Eldorado had sent him into a fit of fury. He had stalked around and around, screaming and banging his fist on the car. Blake could not let it pass without making certain the pimp knew who had done the deed. He left Chiodo's car and walked over to Dudley, saying, "I gotcha, motherfucker." Then they were shouting at each other, nose-to-nose. Blake slugged Dudley, and they wrestled to the street while precinct cops came boiling out of the courthouse. When Officer Trace reached for Blake, the decoy man was smacking Dudley with the blackjack. Trace tried to grab the blackjack, and Blake swung it at his head. The patrolman went down. They dragged Blake into the courthouse, leaving Dudley moaning and bleeding in the street. Officer Trace, with only a bruise on the cheek, helped subdue Blake. Two policemen helped Dudley to his feet, but the pimp refused medical aid. He and the girls went away in a taxi.

As they left the courthouse an hour later, the Eldorado was being towed away, and Chiodo knew that the incident was being hushed up. He also sensed that this was the last they would see of Dudley the Pimp. Mayhew agreed.

"Street justice," Chiodo mused. "Sometimes it works."

"That's one less," Blake muttered.

"Come on, Tommy, let's get you out of here, you crazy dumb donkey Irishman."

In the gutter lay a smashed pair of mirrored glasses.

191

12

Chinatown Encounter

The TPF room was quiet. Pat Mayhew wondered about his partner. Chiodo seemed deep in thought. Finally, two words broke the silence.

"Sword canes," Chiodo said.

Mayhew gave him a quizzical stare. "What did you say?"

"Sword canes. The Chinese supershivs. They're illegal now, you know."

"Since when?"

"Since about a week ago, dummy. It's one of the new amendments to the Penal Code."

"So what? Don't tell me you want to go after sword-cane collars, Chi."

"Maybe."

Chiodo abruptly changed the subject. He drew the .38 from its holster and held it out to Mayhew. "Look, another new stock. That's the third one in a year."

"What the hell are you always buying new stocks for?" Mayhew said. "I would have just taped the damn thing. You're

192

spending more money on guns than the job pays. If you were gonna buy a new stock, you should have gotten a rubber stock. Some guy's just going to make you drop it again."

"Yeah, if I keep working with you I'll probably wind up in the rubber-gun squad anyway, riding some desk in the property clerk's office."

"Well, there are worse things than a broken stock—"

"Right," Chiodo said. "I guess I'm lucky some uniformed guy hasn't blown a hole in my head already. I'm not sure I'd give some skel the chances they've given me. We've got a lot of commemorative plaques hanging in station houses for cops who gave the other guy a break."

Chiodo put the .38 back into its holster, went to the mirror and smoothed his hair. He hoped Sergeant Drackus would not notice that the hair was clean and combed and the beard freshly trimmed. The sergeant had an eye for subtle changes. But then, why should they worry? The decoys were doing well. Chiodo alone had 14 arrests this month. The 35 men under Sergeant Joe Drackus led the city in numbers. Drackus himself was in line for a commendation. The captain was happy, the inspector was happy, and the commissioner basked in friendly headlines. They deserved to have a party. Chiodo's change of clothes hung in the car, as did Mayhew's. For now, he wore the faded fatigue jacket and old dungarees. He and his partners should have waited, though, to splash on the shaving lotion. Pretty smells were an oddity in the basement squad room.

"Hey, Pat, about those sword canes. I know where we can make a good bust."

"Are you crazy? What's a sword-cane bust? That's no great collar."

"How about if we bust a shop that's got a whole load of sword canes?"

"That might be different."

"I've got a shop in mind in Chinatown. I'd like to take it tonight."

"You know we can't do it tonight."

"If we get right out there we could bust the place, make night court and still be back in time."

"Naw, not tonight. Everybody's been planning this party for days."

"Well, I heard some other decoy guys talking about making a sword-cane bust like I'm telling you about. If they make it before we do, there'll be no more sword canes in Chinatown. I really think this would be a good bust."

"It can wait till tomorrow night. Old hot-rocks Blake ain't about to go after sword canes tonight. He's got other things on his mind."

As they waited for roll call, talk filled the TPF room. Juan Hernandez, a Puerto Rican TPF man, dropped in to visit a friend in decoy. Lean, mustachioed and good-natured, Hernandez was a favorite butt of squad-room humor.

"Hey, Juan, I hear there was a terrible accident at your house."

"Yeah? What you hear, Irish?"

"I hear the bed fell down and twenty-two people got injured."

Juan's reply filtered through the guffaws. "It's nice in a Puerto Rican family. We all got a bed to sleep in. We don't have to sleep in the bathtub like you drunken Irish donkeys."

"Guess what I caught the other night, Juan," said Charlie Ficelli. "Got me a first-class jello Jebby, the original Puerto Rican mystery."

"You mean a Yellow Chevy, Charlie?"

"That's what I said, a jello Jebby. Must have cost five thousand dollars—two hundred fifty for the car and forty-five hundred worth of mudguards and tail pipes."

"Har, har, har."

"Must have been a cold night, Charlie. You didn't want to stay on the street?"

"Naw. I knew if I stopped the jello Jebby it'd take me eight hours at the office tracing the owner. I was right. This guy, he looks up at me and says, 'Offeesir, thee car she is belong my brother-in-law, he give it to my cousin who buy the license, and the registration she is in my oncle's name, because . . .'"

Chiodo listened to the talk. "Don't say nothing about jello Jebbies," he said. "I really did put some poor bastard in jail five days one time. It was this gypsy cab, and the VIN tag checked out stolen. What the hell, I got me a GLA, right? The driver keeps saying, 'No, no, man. I buy thees car from the city. You check. You check.' So I lock him up. Five days later his hearing comes up and he produces a sales receipt from the city auction. They'd sold him a fucking stolen car. I felt real bad because, aside from the ten other violations he had, the guy was not a car thief. I felt so bad I took him to lunch."

"You're all heart, Chi," someone said.

"Yeah, Chi, you'd arrest your own mother to stay on top of the sheet for the month."

Sergeant Drackus strode into the room, frowning. He pondered his clipboard and cleared his throat. "All right, pipe down!" The talk stilled. The sergeant stood in the middle of the room, surrounded by his 18 duty men. The quiet became intense. The sergeant's nose wiggled. The sergeant sniffed.

"What's that fucking smell?"

No one replied. The mild eyes moved from face to face. "Smells like a whorehouse in here. Who took a bath in shaving lotion?" The eyes stopped at Charlie Ficelli and studied the short-sleeved shirt with the button-down collar and the necktie. "What's up, Charlie? You ain't working for the city tonight?"

"Uh—yeah, sarge. Sure I'm working. I had an idea I'd work the One-eight. I hear there's a lot of tourists being mugged, so I thought tonight I'd be a tourist."

Normally this would have brought derisive laughter. The 18th Precinct was noted for its flocks of student nurses, and Charlie Ficelli was notorious with nurses. There was no laughter. Drackus frowned. "Stay out of the One-eight, Ficelli, you'll just get in trouble."

Quickly the sergeant assigned his men to teams for the night. Radiomen picked their portables out of the rack and read off the numbers. When he had finished listing the radios, Drackus put his clipboard down on a desk.

"Okay, we've been doing pretty good on collars this month, but it's no time to let up. We're still getting complaints on assaults and strong-arm robberies. Let's get some more strong-arm collars. Any questions?"

There were none.

"Okay, go on out to post."

The men filed out quietly. Drackus stood watching them, arms folded. The sergeant's jaw muscle twitched. Something was in the wind, and it wasn't shaving lotion.

By nine o'clock there wasn't a decoy man on the street in Manhattan South. In a suite of rooms at the Statler the party was just beginning to warm up. The two dozen TPF men present, some of whom had come downtown on their nights off, already were outnumbered by young women, invited and uninvited. Pat Mayhew savored his first VO of the evening and surveyed the scene happily. "One thing I've never been able to understand is how the word gets around to the chicks."

"Yeah, well, just be grateful for small miracles," Chiodo said.

They had made the arrangements several days earlier. Charlie Ficelli had flashed the shield at the desk. "Need a suite, upper floor."

The desk clerk smiled. "Will you be wanting extra ice?"

"Lots of ice."

Rock music blasted from a record player. A girl in skintight pants was doing the frug. Charlie stood with Chiodo and Mayhew, sipping a scotch and water. "Charlie, you're alone tonight? How come?"

"My chick couldn't make it."

"Did you have a spat?"

"Yeah, something like that."

Within 30 minutes the lights were down and the crowd had

thickened. Someone brought in a case of champagne. Magically, a volunteer hostess in black short shorts appeared, serving hors d'oeuvres from a tray. The inevitable clusters formed, telling cop stories. Chiodo drifted into a group around Paul Balakes, a tall, black-haired TPF man from the Bronx with a blonde on his arm.

"I was up in Brooklyn court the other day," Balakes was saying. "My damned case was so far down the docket I needed a shovel to dig it out. So I'm killing time sitting in on trials. This big black old lady comes in with a bunch of hookers. She's charged with prostitution, too. And, man, she looked bad, a real dog. Knife scars all over her face, hair in splotches, must have weighed two-fifty. She's standing before the judge, and the DA's reading off the charge. Prostitution. So she starts yelling something at the judge, and the young legal-aid guy defending her is getting nervous. 'Don't say nothing,' he says. 'Keep quiet. I do the talking.' So he tells the judge, 'Your Honor, there must be some mistake. This woman is fifty-seven years old. She's never been arrested before.' The judge looks down at the DA, and the DA says, 'Well, Your Honor, that's the charge, and here she is in court.' The judge looks at the woman and says, 'I'm going to set bond at fifty dollars.' She nods her head and says, 'Fine, can I say something now?' He says yes. 'Well, Your Judgeship,' she says, 'this here prostitution charge, that's a bunch of shit. Look at me. Who's gonna buy my pussy? Your Judgeship, I'm so bad I can't give it away!' The court broke up. They had to take a twenty-minute recess. The judge fell off the bench."

Chiodo lost count of his drinks. The party swirled around him in a warm blur. Faces appeared and vanished. People talked at his ear and clutched at his arm. The world was rosy, softly lit, filled with perfumes and women's laughter. The busy door kept opening, bringing more guests. As a man and woman walked in, Charlie Ficelli's drink stopped halfway to his lips. He gave a low whistle. "Man, wouldn't I love to play hide the baloney with that."

She was a striking brunette, trim-waisted and tall, eyes blue and cool. Her hair tumbled in luxuriant waves and was caught in front by a band of pearls. She wore something powdery blue and trailed an airy perfume.

"Who's the guy with her?"

"Don't know. Looks like a detective I seen in the One-eight. Nobody invited him, that's for sure."

As the time passed and the party grew louder, Chiodo saw that Ficelli's eye kept drifting to the brunette. He danced with this girl and that one, catching the blue eyes with passing glances and offering his little winking grin. The blue eyes widened and flicked away. The brunette's escort was drinking straight bourbon. The bourbon and Ficelli's attentions were souring his mood. Soon he was haranguing his date in a corner. Ficelli watched from a distance and frowned. "If you're going to act like an ass, I'll just leave," the brunette was saying. She picked up her handbag, but the detective snatched it away.

"You're not going anyplace."

"Oh, yes I am!" Her hand flashed upward with a stinging slap. The detective slapped her back. Ficelli moved in smoothly, grinning, taking the man by the arm, chatting pleasantly, calming things. The brunette stayed, but the peace did not last. Chiodo soon heard them quarreling again.

"All right, go fuck yourself, bitch," the detective said, and stalked away from her. Ficelli hurried to the woman's side. They talked, laughed, drank and danced, watched sullenly from the corner by her date. The brunette picked up her handbag again, and she and Charlie started for the door, pushing through the crowd.

"Just where the hell do you think you're going?"

A drunken roundhouse right grazed Charlie's face. The decoy man sidestepped, then ripped a short, savage punch to the detective's stomach. Glass shattered, and people scurried clear as the two locked in a swaying, panting struggle. The detective brought a knee up, but missed. The side of Ficelli's open hand chopped him across the neck, and the detective toppled across the couch and stayed there, shaking his head. Then Charlie and the brunette were gone, leaving a roomful of dazed people staring at the man on the couch.

"All right, the floor show's over," shouted Chiodo. "Who needs a fresh drink?"

The party resumed, even louder than before. One of the women stripped off her blouse and did a topless dance, breasts jiggling frantically. Couples paired off in the smoky gloom. The detective vanished.

It was after one o'clock when Ficelli and the brunette returned. Lipstick smeared Charlie's face, and he had lost his necktie. He glared around the room.

"Where is that prick? I want to straighten his ass good this time."

"He's gone, Charlie. He left."

"I'm gonna find him and fix him good."

"No, Charlie," purred the brunette. "Don't leave me."

Someone shoved a drink into Charlie's hand. The brunette ruffled his hair and kissed him on the ear. Soon they were dancing again, locked together to the throb of slow rock. The heavy beat measured off passing time.

"Hey, it's two o'clock!"

"Who gives a damn?"

"Drackus will give a good damn. If we don't get back to return roll call he'll be climbing the walls."

"Ficelli's his fair-haired boy. Let Ficelli call him. Hey, Charlie, you gotta call Drackus."

Ficelli snickered happily. "What'll I call him?"

"Come on, Charlie, he'll have the whole fucking TPF out looking for us."

Ficelli went into the next room and made his call to Drackus. No one heard the conversation. He came back with a wave and a belch. "S'all right. Ole Charlie fixed it up. S'all okay."

Chiodo was not too clear later about how they arrived in

Central Park. He remembered vaguely one of the girls, a thin, mousy blonde named Priscilla, saying something about going skinny-dipping.

"Hell, there's no place to go skinny-dipping," someone else had said. "Besides, it's cold outside."

A third voice chimed in: "There's the lake in Central Park."

So in the middle of the night, eight people had packed into a car and headed for the park. Wedged in the back seat beneath a stoutish redhead was the big Irishman, John Banion, guarding his half gallon of red wine. Tommy Blake had materialized from somewhere, his hand stroking Priscilla's thigh. Mayhew snored in the front seat beside Chiodo, who balanced the brunette on his lap while Ficelli drove. The brunette kept flinging her arms around Chiodo's neck and murmuring in his ear, "Charlie, Charlie, I really dig you." He tried to tell her he wasn't Charlie, that Charlie was driving. . . .

"Hey, Charlie," mumbled Blake, "Chi's making it with your chick."

"Naw, not Chi," said Charlie. "He don't know what a strange piece of ass looks like."

"The other night Charlie got a strange piece," Banion said. "He went home and screwed his old lady. Hah, hah, hah."

"Here we are, kids."

Then Priscilla was running down the slope to the lake, shedding her skirt, blouse, bra and bikini panties. Banion lumbered along behind her, ripping off his clothes and pausing to gurgle from the wine bottle. Tommy remained in the car, now fondling the fat redhead. Mayhew snored in the front seat. Ficelli and the brunette slipped away to a dark spot behind a bush, from where there soon came the sounds of heavy breathing and delighted female squeals. Chiodo sat down in the grass and lit a cigarette, watching the moonlit forms of Priscilla and Banion frolic in the lake.

The police car crept up silently with its lights out. Chiodo was not aware of its presence until the spotlight splashed onto the lake and a young uniformed patrolman came striding down the slope, saying, "All right, what's going on here? How many times have we got to chase you hippies out of here. No swimming in the park." In the car his partner moved the spotlight over Banion and Priscilla. They smiled and waved.

Chiodo stumbled to his feet. "We're on the job," he said, fumbling for his shield. "TPF decoys."

"You've gotta be kidding."

The young patrolman inspected their shields and shook his head. "I don't believe it."

"Okay, call the Eighteenth Precinct station. They'll tell you."

At a nearby pay phone the patrolman dialed the precinct office and spoke to the desk lieutenant. "Have you got a decoy unit working out of there? . . . Let me speak to somebody in their office. . . . Closed? Well, how about a roster? Have you got a roster? . . . No roster. Uh—well, is one of their guys about six-two, long reddish hair, big jaw, goes by the name of Banion? . . . Yeah? Another guy is dark, long black hair, black beard, looks like a hippie, calls himself Chi. . . . Yeah? Well, I'll be damned. . . . Uh—nothing. Just checking, that's all." He hung up. "Well, I'll be damned."

The two patrolmen lingered and chatted while Priscilla and Banion put on their clothes and Ficelli and the brunette came back from the bushes. One of the patrolmen tried to get Priscilla's phone number. They declined Banion's offer of wine. Then they left, saying, "See you around."

It was dawn when Chiodo pulled into the driveway at home and fumbled for his key.

Roll call that evening was a somber affair. Men drifted in pale and hollow-eyed. There was no loud banter in the TPF room. Drackus did not join them for the usual exchange of small talk before roll call. At six o'clock sharp he marched in grimly, slapping the clipboard against his thigh.

"All right, quiet."

The men stood or sat, looking solemn. In the back of the room someone hiccuped. Drackus seemed to be trying desperately to control a cauldron of inner emotions. His eyes were two bits of steel set in a mask of stone. When he spoke again, it was with icy deliberation.

"You—you fucking guys."

Drackus spun on his heel to face a pouchy-eyed Charlie Ficelli. The sergeant's face reddened. "And YOU! You got better brains than that!"

"What's the matter, sarge? I called you, didn't I?"

"Yeah, yeah, you called me, you dumb-ass guinea. And what did you tell me?"

"I—uh—told you we got tied up because we—uh—had a flat tire."

"A flat tire! You can't be that stupid. You expect me to believe there were eighteen of you in ONE CAR?"

"Sorry about that, sarge," Ficelli said lamely. "I didn't think of it."

"I knew you guys were fucking around town. Okay, you know my philosophy. You work hard, you play hard. But what if something big had happened last night? Where would I find you? What if the inspector had come around, or somebody from the commissioner's office? Where would my ass be today?"

Then, with a fury exceeding even the tongue-lashing he had given Chiodo the night of Tommy's brawl with the doctor, Drackus erupted. His voice rose and fell in righteous rage. He called the thunder down upon them, flung curses like brickbats, stomped and fumed and sweated. The 15-minute tirade poured over them like molten lava. Even such veterans as Ficelli, Blake, Banion and Mayhew were slack-jawed in amazement.

Then, spent at last, Drackus strode to a desk and sat down heavily in the chair, burying his face in his hands. Somewhere in the ancient station house a toilet flushed. The sound was magnified in the silence of the TPF room.

"And the worst fucking thing is—" The voice was something between a croak and bleat now. Drackus lifted his head with an

202

expression of deep, soulful hurt, "—you didn't even invite me."

The tension broke.

When the men filed out, Chiodo was still changing clothes. Somehow, he did not seem to be functioning properly. Tom Blake eyed his partner coolly. "You look like a zombie."

"And you?" Chiodo replied. "What do you think you look like, a spring daisy?"

"Do you want to catch tonight, or go sleep under a bridge?"

"Tell him, Pat."

"Chi wants to go make a sword-cane collar."

"Uh-huh."

When Mayhew had finished explaining, Blake still looked puzzled. "Well, if sword canes are illegal, how come they're still selling 'em?"

"I'll tell you why," Chiodo said. "Good Chinese cooking and friendly persuasion, that's why. These super-Chinamen keep the precinct cops so soft-soaped and well fed they wouldn't bust a shopkeeper if he peddled sword canes dripping with human blood."

"Have you been eating hot peppers again?"

"No. Me and Pat had a talk with a Fifth Precinct cop in Killy's the other night, remember? The hairbagger was saying all this crap about how they've got to work with the neighborhood, they got to live with the people, it's okay to take a gift now and then. Later on I got to thinking. How the hell could we stick it to some of these guys? Well, Fifth Precinct, Chinatown, sword canes—"

"Let's go," Blake said.

Twenty minutes later they were riding down Mott Street through the lights, babble and restless humanity of Chinatown. Signs clamored for attention in English and Chinese, advertising restaurants, novelty shops and hand laundries. Even the lightpoles and phone booths managed to look Chinese, and Chiodo knew that some of the side streets were too narrow for automobiles.

Nowhere in the city did the people live more densely packed, and yet there was remarkably little crime committed by the Chinese themselves. Muggings, robberies and assaults were largely committed by non-Chinese. Because of rigid, tightly knit family life, built around hard work, honesty and thrift, even juvenile delinquency was low compared to that in other parts of the city. Shrewd Chinese merchants, moreover, not only attended to family duties but also maintained excellent relations with the precinct police. The patrolman could take his meals like a warlord, gorging himself on *moo goo gai pan*, shark-fin soup, pigeon wings, bean sprouts, snow peas and flaky mounds of rice, with no thought of payment. Indeed, the mere offer of payment was an insult to the management. In return, the Chinese were generally permitted to indulge their prime passion for gambling. The Chinese numbers flourished, disrupted only by occasional token raids and arrests.

"There it is, on the corner."

Mayhew parked the car, and Blake and Chiodo inspected the display window of the novelty shop. A large green dragon leered down from a shelf, guarding his cache of porcelain cups, silk scarves and pillows, teak letter openers and bamboo place mats stamped "Made in Hong Kong." There were no sword canes.

"Chi, you're nuts. Where are the canes?"

"Come on, let's go inside."

The tinkling of the door chimes brought an elderly Chinese woman from behind a curtained enclosure.

"Do you have sword canes?"

The face was blank. "Slawd cahn?"

"Sword canes." Chiodo went through the motions of drawing a sword from a cane, waving it in the air, thrusting it back into the scabbard and walking away.

"Oh, man," Blake muttered.

"Ah," said the woman, smiling and nodding. "Slawd cahn!" She vanished through the curtain and returned bearing a sword cane. Blake went around the counter and through the curtain.

The woman scolded him in Cantonese. Blake poked his head back through the curtain. "There must be three hundred sword canes back here."

"Who owns the store?" Chiodo asked the woman.

She shook her head. Chiodo showed his shield. "Then we'll have to arrest you."

The woman's English quickly improved. "I make phone call, okay? See if owner he come."

They waited. Nothing happened. After 15 minutes Chiodo took the woman by the arm. "I hate to do this, but let's go."

Mysteriously, a crowd had gathered outside. As they walked the woman toward the corner, Chinese pressed around them, raising an angry babble. Mayhew worked his way through from the car. "This is no good, Chi. These people are coming out of the woodwork."

They retreated back into the shop and closed the front door.

"Tommy, call the house for a car."

Blake found a telephone and made the request for minor assistance. In less than a minute they heard sirens. A patrol car arrived outside. Then another. And another.

"What the hell?"

As flashing lights filled the street, a muscular sergeant pushed through the crowd and into the shop. "All right, what's going on here?"

Chiodo explained. The sergeant's eyes narrowed. "Damn you decoy guys, why don't you stay outta my precinct?"

"We're taking her in, sarge."

"Taking her in for what?"

"Like I said, they're selling sword canes. In the back there are over three hundred sword canes."

"What's illegal about sword canes? That's a fucking souvenir."

"Sarge, there was a change in the Penal Code. This is against the law under section—"

"You gotta be full of shit. There's nothing wrong with sword canes. They've been selling 'em for years. You're not taking anybody. Now get the hell out of here."

Through the front door walked a neat, smiling Chinese man dressed impeccably in a gray business suit. "What's the trouble, Sergeant Mallock?" The voice was pleasant.

"Nothing, Mister Wong. Just a little misunderstanding. Don't worry about it."

The sergeant pulled Chiodo aside. "Now listen, decoy man, the owner of this store is one of the most important businessmen in Chinatown. He also delivers a lot of votes and keeps things nice and quiet. Savvy? You just get your ass out of here and let us handle it."

"Sergeant, if you want to handle it, just call Inspector Sullivan, TPF. I'll give you his home number. Straighten it out with him."

The sergeant frowned. "Sullivan told you to come down and take this place?"

Chiodo looked at him levelly. "Sullivan himself told us to come down and take this place."

The sergeant paced the floor, muttering. He wiped a meaty hand over his face. Outside the lights flashed atop half a dozen waiting patrol cars. Chinese faces massed at the windows. Mister Wong stood placidly by the window, saying nothing. The woman had found a chair and sat in silence. The sergeant threw up his hands.

"All right," he said, "take her."

"Sergeant, we want the owner of this store."

"But that's Mister Wong. You can't—"

"All right, then, Mister Wong. We're taking Mister Wong."

The sergeant spun on his heel and stalked out. His patrol car roared away, followed by the other units. The decoy men handcuffed their prisoner and began walking the two and a half blocks to the precinct station. Angry Chinese swirled around them, shouting and blocking the way.

"Let's take him in the car," Blake said. "Why the fuck are we walking?"

"No transporting prisoners in private automobiles," Chiodo replied. "They didn't give us a wagon. I want this one by the book."

Mister Wong stopped and said something to the crowd. They fell silent, and a path cleared. As the walk resumed, the crowd followed quietly. Finally, the double doors of the station closed behind the decoy men and their prisoner, and Chiodo looked up into the face of an unhappy desk lieutenant.

"Lou, we've got this guy for—"

"I know all about it," snapped the lieutenant. "I know all about it. Go ahead, supercop, take him upstairs to the detectives. I don't want to hear nothing."

"Thank you very much, sirrrr."

As they headed for the stairway a uniformed patrolman sidled up to Tom Blake. "You guys sure know how to fuck up a meal ticket," the patrolman said.

Blake flushed. "That's right, buddy. Look, if you don't make enough on this job, why don't you apply for welfare. Then you can get two checks for doing nothing."

Chiodo glanced at the wall clock. It was 8:30 P.M. He whispered to Blake, "We've got an hour and a half before night court closes. After that it's too late for arraignment. Their meal ticket will have to spend the night in jail. Got that?"

"That's a good idea."

The writing of arrest cards was always a slow business. Technically it was the detective's chore, but detectives seldom minded if the arresting officer did the work instead. In the 5th Precinct squad room, however, four detectives waited, and the air was charged with efficiency. As Chiodo sat down to begin filling out cards, a detective cried, "Hey, that's our job." Suddenly all four detectives were at work, one man typing arrest cards in four copies, another filling out the DD-19 form, another taking the silent prisoner for fingerprinting.

"What's the rush?" Chiodo said.

A lieutenant hurried up the stairs. "You guys finished with the paper work yet? We've got to get this man to court right away."

As if by magic, the processing was almost complete. Chiodo checked the cards with meticulous care, taking his time.

"Uh—you spelled my name wrong. It's C-h-i, not C-h-o. . . ."

"Look, it's good enough," said a detective. "Take it and get him to court."

"No. We've got to get these things accurate, you know. Better redo the card and spell it right."

Hurriedly a detective made the correction. Chiodo examined the card again. "This address doesn't seem right. Tommy, check the phone book, see if we've got the correct address. Better yet, go back to the store and . . ."

Mister Wong waited patiently. He smiled at Chiodo. "I'm sorry to put you to so much trouble," he said.

"GET THAT MAN TO COURT!" bellowed the lieutenant.

"All right, we're leaving now, lou."

The time was 9:02. There was still a great deal of processing to do. Fingerprint cards had to be dropped off at the identification office, the complaint filled out, the FBI yellow sheet returned. So much to do. Chiodo whistled a peppy tune as they strolled to the switchboard. "We need a wagon," he told the policewoman. She put in the call. They sat down to wait.

At 9:20 the lieutenant appeared. "What the hell are you guys doing still here?"

"Waiting for a wagon, lou."

"You don't need no wagon. You guys make arrests here all the time. Hell, I've seen you walk 'em to court. It's only three blocks."

"Regulations, lou. You know that. It's against the rules to walk a prisoner to court."

"All right, then, get a car. Get a car. We've got to get this man to court."

"Yeah, but we've still got to drop off the prints at CIB."

"Don't worry about it." The lieutenant seemed oddly short of breath. "We'll take care of that." Quickly he instructed a driver to drop one decoy man off at the Criminal Identification Bureau with the prints and rush the others to court. "Okay, now take him in a car."

"All right, if you're ordering me to violate regulations by transporting a prisoner in a car, then I've got to have it in writing. You'll have to make a notation on my book."

With slashing strokes of his pen, the lieutenant made the notation and signed it. "There!" Then he hurried away, mopping his face with a pocket handkerchief.

Mayhew and Blake took the prisoner to the court building in a radio car while Chiodo was dropped off at the CIB office with the fingerprint cards. It was 9:45 when he walked up to the clerk's desk.

"Man, these are coming in late," said the clerk. "I don't see how you're going to make court tonight."

"You're going to get a call to rush verification of these prints," Chiodo said. "Forget it. I don't want them back tonight. I don't have to make night court."

"Okay, that's easy. I'll just put them at the bottom of the pile."

Chiodo's partners were waiting for him outside the courthouse. "Let's go get a beer," he told them. "We're home free."

At 10:30 they finished their beers at the corner café. Chiodo pushed back from the table. "Well, might as well make an appearance in court. Formality, you understand. Then we'll pick up Mister Wong and find him some nice iron lodgings for the night."

An anxious clerk was waiting as the partners strode into the complaint room of the courthouse.

"Are the prints back on Wong?" Chiodo asked.

"Yeah, they just came over by special messenger."

Chiodo telephoned the CIB man. "Hey, how come such sudden service on Wong? You said you'd put him at the bottom of the pile."

"Listen, buddy, I got a call to rush 'em. If those prints weren't in court pronto, I was in trouble."

They went to the complaint desk. "Too late to draw up a complaint tonight, right?"

"Yeah, too late," said the clerk. "Wait a minute, have you got—?"

"Yeah, we've got him."

In night court the judge was waiting, the clerk was waiting, the FBI yellow sheets were ready—showing two previous arrests, one in 1940 for illegal entry as an alien and another for selling fireworks—and Mister Wong sat smiling in his business suit. Swiftly the judge released him on his own recognizance.

The merchant walked out chatting amiably with the decoy men. "I'm sorry to put you gentlemen to all that trouble. Why don't you come to my restaurant and we'll have a fine Chinese dinner."

"No thanks, Mister Wong," Chiodo said, "but we do appreciate the offer."

"Any time," Mister Wong said. "Policemen are our very, very special friends."

They waited until he caught a cab and waved good-bye.

Blake looked at Chiodo and shook his head.

"Well," Chiodo said, "what's on your fucking mind?"

"I guess they're right, Chi."

"What do you mean?"

"If you can't beat 'em, join 'em."

"Bullshit."

13

The Turnstile

Patches of ice glazed the streets. A bitter wind swept off the East River into the canyons of Manhattan. Pedestrians rushed along hunched in heavy coats. Chiodo found a parking space near the courthouse and hurried inside, grateful for the warmth. He would spend the day in court and take that night off. Let somebody else freeze in the streets for a change. A man had to get the ice cubes melted from his blood. A confrontation with lawyer Lewis would warm him quickly enough. If lawyer Lewis went too far—who knows? Officer Chiodo might make a collar right in the courthouse.

"Patrolman Chiodo?" The man detached himself from the wall of the lobby, hand extended. "I'm Arnold Lewis." Chiodo ignored the hand.

"How do you do."

"You don't like attorneys?" The smile was oily, the eyes small and closely set above a pencil-line mustache.

"I don't shake hands with attorneys."

"I see. . . ." Lawyer Lewis hesitated. He gave a delicate cough from behind a manicured hand. "About this matter of the Grafton boy. The case has been dismissed. As far as I know it's finished. I don't see why you are pursuing it."

"I'm not sure either," Chiodo said. "But if there has been anything underhanded or illegal in this, I'd want to know about it."

The eyebrows lifted. "That's a rather serious implication. Are you a detective?"

"No, I'm not a detective. I'm a cop, a plain, ordinary cop, and I want to know what went on."

"As far as I know, you failed to appear in court on the dates set for trial, and the case was dismissed."

Chiodo frowned and shook his head.

From the beginning he had sensed a change in procedure in the Grafton case. The boy came from a prominent New Jersey family. Chiodo and Mayhew had arrested him on Eighth Avenue for possession of marijuana—half a dozen hand-rolled cigarettes and an additional supply in a small plastic bag. Lawyer Lewis had appeared on the day scheduled for trial and asked for a postponement. The tactic was common. In granting the request the judge normally would have said, "Officer, give me a date." Then he would have asked the defense attorney if the new date was satisfactory. In the Grafton case no alternate date was set. The clerk merely told Chiodo, "You will be notified."

Six weeks passed, and no summons arrived in the brown interdepartmental envelopes at the TPF room. Chiodo, wondering if there had been an oversight, went to the court records. The clerk told him the case had been dismissed. "Apparently it was set for trial on three separate occasions and you didn't show up, officer." He gave Chiodo the dates. The next morning Chiodo was on the phone to lawyer Lewis. Their conversation had not cleared the air.

"Officer, you did your job," Lewis had said. "Now just forget it, huh?" When Chiodo threatened to go to the district attorney,

Lewis had arranged the meeting in the courthouse lobby. And now the lawyer stood there glancing at his watch, as if to indicate that his time was precious and their business concluded.

"Mister Lewis, I'm going to the DA. I don't know if it's your fault or the court's fault or anybody's fault. All I know is, I never received a subpoena and there's something fishy about this whole thing."

"Officer, I wouldn't do that if I were you."

"Why not?"

"Let's just say that this case has certain—uh—political overtones and it wouldn't do you or me any good to pursue it further. There are people involved who are more important than either of us."

"Great. That makes it even more interesting. I'll tell you what. I was going to put off going to the DA's office for a few days but I've changed my mind. I'm going up there right now."

"Don't do anything hasty."

"Why? Do you have something more to tell me?"

"As a matter of fact, I might have something to tell you that would be very interesting. Let's go across the street for a cup of coffee."

"Tell me now. I don't want to go for a cup of coffee."

Lewis glanced around the lobby. "What I want to tell you I can't tell you here."

"Why?"

"What I have to tell you might have a way of changing your —uh—point of view. You might not wish to pursue this further."

"How are you going to do this?"

"I can't tell you here."

Chiodo laughed. "Do you know what, counselor? I think what you have in mind is to take me for coffee and slip me a few dollars. I'm going to save you the grief of being arrested. If there's anything else you've got to say, say it now and we'll forget about crossing the street."

The lawyer's mouth drew into a thin line. "If that's the way you feel about it," he said, "then go to the DA's office. But it won't do you any good." He turned and walked away.

Lewis was right. In the district attorney's office Chiodo talked to a preoccupied assistant prosecutor whose reaction was total indifference. Only after Chiodo had hammered his fist on the desk would the man even jot down the arrest, case and docket numbers on Grafton. A month passed with no action. He went back to make another inquiry, this time with a different prosecutor. On his third trip an administrative assistant offered him a cigarette, lit it and said quietly, "Officer Chiodo, we have looked into the Grafton case thoroughly. It is the opinion of the district attorney's office that to reopen it would be a waste of the taxpayers' money."

One learned to live with the setbacks. The early frustrations of losing small battles no longer galled him. The court system was, in its way, a leveler. He won far more than he lost; his convictions were running high. In a single month he had spent 14 days in court; in another month, 13 days. There was always the option of taking the night off, but he preferred to work. The game was numbers, and the numbers were in the street. Some of his old cases were still being tried, or awaiting trial, in Brooklyn's courthouse. New cases were coming up in Manhattan. He alternated between the two, mingling with the throngs of waiting lawyers, witnesses, cops and defendants. The courthouse was humanity in all its forms, a concentration of all the life from the streets, the shops, the taverns, the tenement slums and the homes and apartments of the well-to-do. Hippies, Puerto Ricans, businessmen, blacks, housewives, junkies, drunks, whores, doctors, they were all here and more. The parade was endless in its variety and fascination.

On court days Chiodo liked to arrive early, around nine o'clock. He filled out his forms at the police desk, got his ticket with the time stamp, checked the calendar for the number of his case and then had his morning coffee, to help wash the fatigue from his mind. One could make do on five hours' sleep, but it took concentration. With hundreds of cases crowding the dockets, there was time to kill. He sat in on trials, following the legal skirmishing, the tiresome haggling over technicalities, the bizarre defense maneuvers to block evidence.

Presiding in the austere, musty courtrooms were good judges and bad, honest, fair-minded judges and political hacks, judges who could be greased, and judges who could not. In time he came to recognize the subtleties at work in hearings and trials. The world of judges, lawyers and clerks, after all, was ironically similar to the world of the street: There were good guys and bad guys.

"Hey, I've got another case in Manhattan this afternoon. I'd like to get there by two-thirty. This Robinson case has got a low number and I'm the arresting officer. Do you think we can get it called pretty soon?"

He was in the Brooklyn court. A bored clerk looked up from his papers. "Sit down. Your turn will come."

Chiodo waited. An hour went by. Several cases lower on the docket were called. He was not naïve. A five-dollar bill to the clerk would speed things. Some officers paid. Chiodo had no intentions of paying. The time-honored practice of greasing the clerk to get one's case called was nettlesome and unfair. There were clerks who took the grease, and clerks who did not, and this man was a taker. Chiodo stalked back to the desk.

"Listen, prick," he said quietly, "I know what's going on in this court. I'm not giving you two cents and I want this case called. Furthermore, if I see you take a dime, or even look like you might take one, I'll arrest you right here in this court."

The clerk's head jerked up. "You're full of shit," he retorted. "Sit down and wait your turn."

The clock crept toward the lunch hour, passed it and dragged into the afternoon. Chiodo ground his teeth. The clerk walked past him. He jumped up and pulled the man aside. "If I see you on the street you're in trouble."

The clerk's eyes widened. "You're threatening me!"

"Yes, I'm threatening you."

The man vanished briefly then returned. "Judge Angliotti wants to see you in his chambers."

The judge was a florid man with double chins and a shock of black hair. Despite the somber black robes and the setting of lawbooks and polished woods, he had the look of a friendly ward politician. But in court Angliotti was a fair man. "Officer, I know you do a good job and I see you in court a lot," he said, "but what's this about you threatening my clerk?"

"Judge, can I talk to you man-to-man?"

"Yes."

"That guy's a prick. I know what goes on in this court. Favors are done for certain people, and other people go to the bottom of the pile. You're too busy to notice such things, but they go on all the time. If I wanted to get out of this court in a hurry because I had a piece of ass sitting somewhere, that'd be different. But I want to get out of here because I've got another case in Manhattan this afternoon."

"Well, the system is slow. It takes time."

"Your Honor, that's not it. I asked the clerk the first time, then the second time, but this guy is always busting my balls. I'm not even asking any special favors. This case has got a low number and should have been called long before now anyway."

"All right, son, don't get upset. But let me give you some advice. You're lucky I'm here today. Some other judge might react differently and you'd be in a lot of trouble. Just be careful and don't go around threatening people."

"Thank you, Your Honor. Will you call the case for me now?"

"I'll call it as soon as possible."

Another hour went by. As Chiodo again walked up to the desk, the clerk seemed to brace himself. "Are you going to call this case?" Chiodo said. "The judge said he wanted it called."

"You sit down, officer," shouted the clerk, "and stop threatening me!"

216

The outburst interrupted the judge. He called an immediate recess in the case he was hearing and summoned both Chiodo and the clerk to his chambers. "What's the problem now?"

"Your Honor, I went over to ask the clerk here if my case was going to be called. I thought maybe the papers got misplaced or you forgot about it. I was trying to remind him—"

"He threatened me again, Your Honor," the clerk whined.

"I don't want to get into that," said the judge. "You call that case as soon as we get back into court."

"Your Honor, I think this case should be called last," the clerk said.

"I don't care what you think. Call the case."

Within ten minutes the Robinson case was called. The defense lawyer promptly asked for a postponement. "Granted," the judge said.

Chiodo ran out, got into his car and drove to the Manhattan Courthouse. The clerk there checked the docket and shook his head. "I'm sorry, officer, that case was called and you weren't here. The judge ordered a postponement."

The greasing system was a minor irritant, spawned by overcrowded courts and varying shades of ethics. One could not condemn the clerk too harshly, knowing that there were narcotics and vice detectives stashing tin boxes in their closets. It was no secret in the station houses that some plainclothesmen assigned to bookmakers, the numbers racket and prostitution took home as much as $1600 per month per man, and that the division of spoils reached even to inspector rank. Periodic shake-ups would break up the units, sending men back into uniform or transferred to other police boroughs. But like the perennial bad seed, corruption always sprouted afresh. In the courts the pickings, by comparison, were meager indeed.

What troubled Chiodo more deeply was the gross ineffectiveness of a court and jail system that, if anything, tended to breed as much crime as it curbed. At home he expressed this growing awareness to Linda.

217

"I'm beginning to see the pattern, babe. You can start with an eleven-year-old kid. He decides to go lift somebody's wallet to buy himself a flashy bike. It works; he gets away with it. Pretty soon the kid decides to try again, on a larger scale. And the irony is, nobody goes out to commit a crime with the thought of getting caught. So finally this kid is seventeen years old, an accomplished petty thief, and I catch him on the street boosting cars. So where do we put him? For six months he's locked up with the professional burglar with ten years' experience who knows how to crack every safe in town. We put him with the professional mugger who's made two hundred hits before getting caught. We put him with the seasoned drug pusher who instantly recognizes a new recruit to the trade. 'Don't be stupid, kid,' the pusher says. 'You're burglarizing parked cars and candy stores, and for what? Twenty or thirty bucks. I'll show you how to make five, six hundred dollars a day.' So the kid goes back into the street after six months, and all we've taught him is how to become an accomplished thief, or worse. We've made no real effort to get at the reasons behind his crime. If he sees a psychiatrist at all, it's a doctor who's so overwhelmed with cases that he can't begin to look into one head properly, much less five thousand heads. There's nobody to correct that tiny little deficiency that might have triggered some complex in the kid, a hooked nose or a battered ear or crooked teeth—the insignificant little thing that might have set him apart from other people in the first place. Psychologists are discovering that a physical defect can build up more pressure than we ever fully realized before. . . ."

As a cop, his job was to herd them in. The name of the game was numbers. He was developing a philosophy about that, too: "I'll do my job, and the rest of the people will just have to do theirs. If I lock somebody up and the judge lets him go, there's no need to get uptight about it. I'll catch him again."

The complexities of the breakdown in the courts took on awesome dimensions. Chiodo sat in on trials where justice tripped over its own feet so badly that the outcome would have

218

been ludicrous, were it not often so cruel. Seasoned criminals hired the shrewdest lawyers to buy them time. Postponement followed postponement, adding to the glut of cases on groaning court calendars. Finally, in an effort to shove it through and ease the backlog, the district attorney's office agreed to plea bargaining—a guilty plea on a lesser offense instead of a time-consuming jury trial. Then, like John the Limp, the hoodlum did his abbreviated sentence and went back to the street, to steal the money to pay his lawyer.

If such cases represented injustice to society, others were clearly injustice to the accused. A man with a bad past record often found himself in court for a crime he did not commit. Faced with the threat of another long prison term (who, after all, was going to believe a previously convicted felon?), he frequently ended up plea-bargaining, too. A five-year sentence, even for a crime you did not commit, was better than twenty.

But somehow the system rocked along. Despite the crowding, the greasing, the incompetence, the political conniving, the thwarted justice and outright injustice, there were bright spots, too. Chiodo found one of them in a woman judge.

They had made the collars on a bitterly cold night on East Sixth Street, just off Second Avenue. Chiodo, Banion and Mayhew had seen a black youth passing a packet of tinfoil to two white boys. Chiodo grabbed the black. A long-haired blond youth, built like a wrestler, smashed his clasped hands down on Chiodo's arm and broke the grip. The black sprinted down Sixth with Chiodo in pursuit. Slipping on patches of ice, he drew the .38 and fired a shot in the air. The shot gave the fugitive an extra burst of speed. Chiodo cursed, slipping and stumbling on the ice, as the runaway increased his distance. Finally, gasping and wheezing after a torturous foot chase across Broadway traffic, he lost him. When Banion arrived with the car, Chiodo was too winded to speak. They made a brief search along the route of the chase but found nothing. Then they rode back to where Mayhew waited with the other two prisoners.

"What have you got?" Chiodo said.

"A little hash. This blond kid dropped it when we grabbed him."

The blond youth glowered. He was even bigger than Chiodo had thought.

"Great, we'll take 'em in."

"Aw, let them go, Chi," Banion said. "It's not worth the trouble."

"Fuck them. You want to let this scumbag go after what he did? He's in." Chiodo confronted the blond youth. "You're under arrest."

"For what?"

"For possession of hashish."

"What's hashish?"

"Don't give me that shit." Chiodo grabbed him by the collar. "You're under arrest."

The youth tried to push him away. Chiodo, furious, spun him around and shoved him. The youth lost his balance and hurtled against a plate-glass window. "Oh, no!" Mayhew gasped. The window bowed inward but held. As the youth bounced from it, Chiodo was on him, pounding with his fists. Banion dragged him off and handcuffed the prisoner.

During the ride to the station the youth sulked. "Pig, you damn near killed me back there. You won't get away with this kind of brutality. My father—"

"Shut your fucking face."

Edward Carmen's parents came to the station house. They were a quiet, conservatively dressed couple in middle age. Chiodo charged the youth with possession of hashish, harassment, resisting arrest, attempted assault on a police officer and aiding and abetting an escape. The boy was 17, and his yellow sheet showed no previous arrests. "Pure hogwash," the father muttered. "They're always picking on long-haired kids."

Chiodo took the drug samples to the police laboratory, nettled over how the bureaucracy put extra, time-consuming chores on the arresting officer. When the lab reported the sam-

220

ples confirmed and ready, it was also his duty to pick them up and carry them to the property clerk's office. "Damn," he muttered, "we're messenger boys." He did not pick up the lab report.

On the morning scheduled for trial, Edward Carmen appeared with his lawyer. Chiodo expected him to ask for a postponement. The assistant district attorney turned to Chiodo. "Officer, do you have the lab report."

"No, the lab report's not ready yet."

The defense attorney sputtered. "What do you mean no lab report? How do we even know it was *Cannabis?*"

"Counselor," said the judge sternly, "we would have been notified if the report was negative. Officer, I'm going to reset this case. You call the lab and see if it's ready."

"The defense is ready for trial, Your Honor," the lawyer said. "I have a very busy schedule, and we don't want to postpone this case. We've got an open-and-shut case here, and I request that we recall this today."

"Very well, we'll recall it this afternoon."

Chiodo drove to the laboratory on Twenty-third Street, picked up the drugs and the lab report and was back in court by two o'clock. The case was called.

"Officer, do you have the evidence?"

"Yes, Your Honor."

"Is the defense ready to proceed?"

"Your Honor," said the defense attorney, "there has been a new development in this case, and the defense respectfully requests a postponement."

The judge gave the defense attorney a sharp rebuke but granted the postponement. Chiodo took the drug and the lab report to the property clerk's office, an antiquated, loosely administered storehouse of evidence. Controls on impounded drugs were so lax that rumors circulated in the station houses that more than $15 million worth of heroin, seized in the sensational breakup of the so-called French Connection international smuggling ring, had somehow vanished from the property room. Even Chiodo's tiny packet of hashish was promptly misplaced, causing another furor when the Carmen case again came up for trial before a different judge.

"Have you got the evidence, officer?"

"No, Your Honor. The property clerk can't find it."

"Your Honor, this is most exasperating," declared Carmen's attorney. "I move for dismissal on grounds that the prosecution cannot produce the evidence."

"Objection, Your Honor," said the district attorney.

"I'll have it this afternoon, judge," Chiodo said, "if I have to hunt for it myself."

The property clerk found the hashish, and Chiodo carried it with him as he walked into the courtroom. The trial was now set for hearing before its third judge, a woman. The defense attorney immediately asked for another postponement. "We're not ready to go to trial, Your Honor."

"Your Honor," Chiodo blurted out, "this attorney pulled that on me the last time when the junk was in the lab."

"I'll handle this, officer," said the judge. "Counselor, I'm putting this case on for hearing today."

The defense lawyer asked for a conference with Chiodo and the assistant district attorney. As they huddled around a table the lawyer gave them an ingratiating smile. "Look, you really don't have a case here. Why don't you go for a dismissal? The stuff wasn't even found on the kid but on the sidewalk."

"Counselor," said Chiodo, "first of all, this kid's a prick. He gave me a hard time. I'd really like to teach him a lesson. Even if we get a conviction he's not going to do any time. But I want the satisfaction of having his name on a record. Just to make you feel good about it, though, I'd probably be inclined to give him a break if he had a decent lawyer who didn't try to pull these bullshit tricks and treat a cop like he was a piece of dirt. I arrested this kid two months ago. Since then, his being a prick has worn off. Your being a prick hasn't worn off."

"Officer, I don't like to be talked to that way. You've got to talk to an attorney with more respect."

"You don't deserve respect."

"Take it easy," said the prosecutor.

"All right, then," the lawyer sighed. "Do what you will."

In her first term on the bench Judge Margaret Foley was building a reputation for conservatism in her rulings. She also presided with efficiency and detachment. But Chiodo had no illusions about this: Detachment could go either way.

Edward Carmen in court was a vastly different personality from Edward Carmen on the street. Clean-cut, hair clipped and combed, wearing a suit and tie, he had the fresh, sincere look of the president of a Sunday School class. His defense was carefully rehearsed.

"We were just standing and talking when some hippie jumped me."

"Is that hippie in this courtroom?"

"Yes, sir."

"Would you please point him out?"

"That fellow over there." The finger pointed at Chiodo.

"Wait a minute," said the judge. "Is that the arresting officer?"

"Yes, Your Honor."

Carmen's story was that Chiodo and his partners had attacked them, picked up something from the ground and said it was hashish. Yes, he had fought back, because he was not aware that they were police officers. No, he had not seen a black youth running away.

Chiodo then gave his testimony. When both sides had been told, the judge left the courtroom for a brief recess. Chiodo shared the tension as they waited. At last the judge returned with her verdict.

"On the charge of harassment and resisting arrest, I find the defendant not guilty. On the charge of attempted assault on a police officer, I find the defendant not guilty."

Smiles were spreading over the faces of Carmen and his attorney.

"On the charge of possession of *Cannabis,* I find the defendant—guilty."

The smiles collapsed. The attorney was on his feet, shouting. "Your Honor, this verdict is ridiculous. I'm going to appeal this case."

"I find the defendant guilty, counselor. You may appeal if you wish. The defendant is continued on bail until sentencing.

As they were leaving the courtroom, Judge Foley called to Chiodo. "Officer, I'd like a word with you. Come up here, please."

Then they were alone in the annex room. Judge Foley was a petite woman with graying hair and attractive features. In her black robes she reminded Chiodo of an aging student made up for a play. "What kind of a policeman are you?" she asked.

Chiodo explained. She nodded and smiled. "Fascinating."

"Your verdict sort of surprised me," Chiodo said.

"Why? Did you think he would get off?"

"Frankly, I thought he might. If I may ask, why did you find him guilty of possessing hashish and not guilty of assault?" Chiodo liked the judge. He felt comfortable asking the question.

"Well, officer, we realize that sometimes you have to use a certain amount of force in an arrest. You probably know as much law as many lawyers around here. The assault charge can be a device to protect yourself. There are often extenuating circumstances. Were you offended that I did not find him guilty of assault?"

"Not really. There have been some other cases in the past that did offend me, though. The Aliens, for example. Did you read about—?"

"Yes, I remember that case. Some of the judges were discussing it afterward." Judge Foley grew thoughtful. "Did Edward Carmen's parents give you trouble after his arrest?"

"Yes. They came down to the station house very angry. There

224

had been a mistake, their son would never be involved in drugs, he didn't associate with such people, we were harassing him because he had long hair."

"Your own hair isn't exactly short."

"We hear it all the time, though," Chiodo said, "especially from middle-class parents."

Judge Foley nodded. "That's the trouble with this country today. The permissive society. A lot of these kids are spoiled brats. Their parents give them everything. Then when they're in trouble they give them a lawyer. People tend to blame all the wrong things, in my opinion: the schools, the neighborhoods, the police, the courts. But I think it's the parents. That's where the blame should lie. When I see a delinquent kid, ninety-nine times out of a hundred he has negligent or overly-indulgent parents.

Chiodo remarked that Carmen's attorney had not been very clever in his tactics. "He could have taken a guilty plea on a lesser charge, attempted possession. That's the fashion these days, with this turnstile justice."

"Well, obviously he thought he could win the case and bring the boy out of it with a clean record," the judge said. Her thoughts turned to the larger dilemma of the courts. "I'll admit, this certainly isn't the fairest and most efficient system in the world, Officer Chiodo. We do have what some of you fellows call 'turnstile justice.' But right now it's the best we've got, and we have to make it work. Some of us are trying. We're really trying. . . ."

Chiodo walked out of the courthouse mentally refreshed.

14

Riot on Fifth Avenue

It was happening again. The clouds of Vietnam were gathering over New York City. When the storm broke, Chiodo would be in the eye of it. Of that he was certain.

The war was a thing of youth. Its tensions were transmitted to youth as air pressure is to a barometer. Richard Nixon came into the presidency promising an end to it, but endings did not come overnight, and the patience of youth is short. The casualty figures from ground combat slid slowly downward. There were fewer telegrams of regrets, fewer photographs of uniformed young men looking out from the obituary pages. Yet the grim count was still going on, and the violent backlash that had sent Lyndon Johnson into an ignominious retirement continued, a constant, nagging reminder to the new man in the White House. Vietnam fueled the revolt of the middle-class young, spawned out of the frustrations of a burgeoning technological society. The target was authority. Parents represented authority, the financial and industrial establishment represented authority, police represented authority. And now, Richard Nixon was coming to New York City December 9th for a Football Hall of Fame dinner at the Waldorf. In times of lesser ferment the duties of escort would have been ceremonial; in these unsettled times they were grimly defensive.

In the station houses they broke out the blue riot helmets, and men were ordered on standby. Across the city the massive bureaucracy of the police department shifted gears, bracing for crisis. In the basement TPF room with its clutter and steam pipes and musty smells, Joe Drackus briefed his men. All 35 of them were gathered, and the air was close. The sergeant's words were clipped and emphatic.

"The president is making his speech. All days off are cancelled. Some of you will be mingling with the street people in plainclothes. Others will work in uniform." Drackus cast a somber eye over the familiar faces. Many of the faces were covered with whiskers and framed in unruly tangles of uncut hair. He shook his head and sighed. "You'll be a sorry sight in uniform, but it can't be helped."

"What's the deal, sarge? How come some of us have to be in uniform?"

"They want as many guys in uniform as possible. In fact, they want the whole unit in uniform, but I told 'em I'd have to have at least eight or ten men in plainclothes. At least we can be thankful for that. Okay, now here's what we've got so far. The president is supposed to land at the Wall Street Heliport. From there he'll motorcade up FDR Drive to Forty-second Street, then west to Park Avenue and north to the Waldorf Astoria. The information we've got from the Fifth Avenue Peace Committee is that they're expecting the motorcade to come up Fifth. We understand they'll be massing around Saint Patrick's Cathedral, but undoubtedly there will also be a large group outside the Waldorf. TPF will maintain low visibility until we're needed. The squads will be posted in buses on side streets. We'll also have men stationed along the main route, manning temporary command posts at telephones. This will augment radio communications and give us a constant monitoring of crowd activity in specific locations and the progress of the motorcade. If all hell breaks loose—and from the information trickling out of the Peace Committee this is very likely to happen—we will have a busy day, gentlemen. A very busy day." Drackus paused and wiped his face with his hand. "Riot duty on Fifth Avenue," he said. "What's this fucking world coming to?"

Chiodo was at home when he got his call shortly before noon on the ninth. It was Bob Mathes in the TPF office.

"Hey, Chi, I got good news for you. Guess what?"

"I got no time to play guessing games."

"Oh, I caught you in a bad mood, huh? This'll cheer you up. You better dig out the old bag and dust it off. You'll be wearing it tonight."

"What are you talking about? What bag?"

"I got a message from roll call to tell you that you're in uniform tonight. Report to the One-eight at five o'clock."

"Stop busting my balls. That can't be right. I'm not in the bag."

"Really, Chi, that's what it says here. You're in the bag tonight. I'm serious."

For the next three hours he made a series of exasperated telephone calls without success, even to the point of trying to reach Drackus at home. The sergeant was out. Finally he dressed, and looked at the result. It was a bizarre sight. From the neck down, he was again one of New York's finest: pressed, polished and shined. From the neck up, the reflection was that of a bearded, long-haired freak. When he put on the helmet the effect was even worse. Hair protruded wildly around the edge of the helmet, and the beard gave him the look of a fugitive from a motorcycle gang. Chiodo shuddered.

At the TPF squad room Drackus looked up in surprise. "What are you doing in uniform?"

"That was the order, sarge. Report in uniform."

"I wanted you in plainclothes for a special assignment. The demonstrators are meeting at Saint Patrick's. I need you in on it."

"Oh, shit, I didn't bring any other clothes. I told that dumb bastard it was a mistake."

"Well, too late to go back home now. I'll have to send Frank Murphy instead."

Impending action charged the station-house atmosphere. Helmeted men gathered in the old offices. Many of the faces were strange to Chiodo. Commanders he had never seen before also appeared. Brass sparkling, they crowded into offices for urgent conferences. He recognized detectives from outlying precincts, squeezed into uniforms they had not worn in years. Radios crackled with commands.

Flushed with excitement, Chiodo soon found himself in the back of a van with a dozen other men, riding to his post—a phone booth on Forty-second Street and Second Avenue. As he got out, a sergeant gave him instructions. "This is one of the temporary command headquarters' phones, Chiodo. Stay here. When the motorcade comes by, call in. If a crowd gathers in this area, report that too." Then the van was gone and Chiodo was standing there swinging a nightstick, hair protruding from beneath his helmet, a portable radio dangling from his belt.

The presidential motorcade came and went. He caught a fleeting glimpse of black limousines behind a phalanx of motorcycles and surrounded by Secret Service men. A crowd had gathered to watch the procession and then quickly evaporated. Chiodo was alone beside his telephone booth. Time passed slowly.

"This is Patrolman Chiodo, temporary command headquarters Second Avenue. There's nothing happening here."

"Okay. Stay there."

He listened to the radio calls. Action was breaking on Park Avenue. At the hotel 150 demonstrators broke through barricades that had sealed off a four-block area. TPF squads broke them up and pushed them back. Another thousand massed behind the barricades chanting, "Anarchy! Anarchy!" and waving Viet Cong battle flags. Midtown traffic was snarled. Urgent requests for more men crackled from the Saint Patrick's area, and there were reports of department-store windows being smashed. As the tempo increased he heard radio background noises of crowds and sirens. But the phone booth was silent, the street deserted.

"This is Patrolman Chiodo, Second Avenue post. Nothing's going on here at all. How about sending me somewhere else."

"Uh—we can't tell you anything right now, Chiodo. I'll have to find out. Stay there and we'll get back to you."

Another half hour passed. He called again. TPF headquarters was trying to locate Captain McDermott to tell them what to do with Chiodo.

"Where is Captain McDermott now?"

"Out on the street somewhere. We'll call you."

The phone was silent again. In the distance he heard more sirens. His feet ached from standing. He was bored. What a dog of an assignment. They could have put a broom at the phone booth for all the good he was doing. Chiodo, supercop. Hah! Well, they couldn't do this to him. A man could only take so much. Time dragged. He had to do something. He came to a decision. He dialed again.

"Patrolman Chiodo here, Second Avenue. I'm leaving this command post."

"Do you have authority to leave?"

"Yeah."

"Okay."

He walked toward the action. At Fifth Avenue and Fifty-fourth Street a TPF bus sat parked at the curb. Two dozen riot-helmeted men from the Fourth Squad milled around the bus. Others were inside, slouched in the seats. "What are you guys doing here?" Chiodo asked a patrolman.

"We're on call."

They were confused. The Fourth Squad was supposed to be in another location. They had become separated from their sergeant. No one seemed to know just what to do. Chiodo found a telephone and called TPF headquarters.

"What are you doing with the Fourth Squad? What's your location again?"

"Fifth Avenue and Fifty-fourth."

"You're not supposed to be there."

"Yeah, we know that. Where are we supposed to be?"

"I dunno. If you'll wait, we'll get back to you—"

"Don't bother," Chiodo said. "We'll figure something out." He returned to the squad. "All right," he shouted, "everybody back on the bus."

From the barrage of radio reports, violence was raging in front of Saint Patrick's Cathedral. Police units, surrounded and outnumbered by swirling mobs, were calling for reinforcements. At Fiftieth Street and Fifth Avenue, a voice shouted into a microphone, "Dammit, we're being overrun here. Send more men!"

Chiodo turned to the bus driver. "You heard the man," he said. "Let's go." In the bus behind him, heads ducked into helmets and hands tugged at chin straps.

Fifth Avenue swarmed with people. The mob surged upon the intersection of Fiftieth Street, where TPF squads had flung out a line of men. As the bus rolled to a stop and the doors snapped open, Chiodo caught the flash of a steel pipe in the street and a spurt of blood as a policeman went down. Glass shattered in storefront display windows. Bearded hippies raced past the bus, beards flying. Wailing sirens signaled the arrival of more police cars. Ambulances nosed slowly through the crush of people.

The Fourth Squad rolled out of the bus, forming a flying wedge. Their arrival touched off a mass retreat of the crowd. Grimly the TPF men hurled themselves at the screaming mass.

231

A swarthy youth, wild-eyed beneath a tangle of brown hair, swung a two-foot length of steel pipe at Chiodo. A heavy plumber's elbow bulged at the end of the pipe. Chiodo ducked, drove his foot into the attacker's knee and saw him go down, screaming. He pushed ahead.

A car sat in the middle of a cleared space. The crowd seemed to stay back because of the bloody figures there. Frank Murphy leaned over the hood of the car, holding his head. The blood poured from his head, down his neck and his shirtfront. From the waist up, the decoy man was drenched in blood. Joe Drackus, Charlie Ficelli and Paul Bachio hovered around him. Drackus was trying to wipe the blood from Murphy's face. On the ground nearby, two long-haired demonstrators were being pinned down by two other decoy men in plainclothes. Chiodo pushed through to Drackus.

"What happened?"

"These guys must have made Frank. They cracked his head open."

Chiodo swallowed hard. Murphy, after all, had been his replacement. He and Drackus exchanged glances.

"He'll be all right," Drackus said.

The anger made a bitter taste in Chiodo's mouth. Behind him someone shouted, "Fuckin' pig!" One of Murphy's attackers was trying to get up. A decoy man gave his arm a savage twist and he flopped facedown on the sidewalk, moaning.

"Clear this crowd," Drackus shouted to a group of uniformed patrolmen. "Let's clear this street!"

The command galvanized the police. As they formed up for the rush, hippies fled in all directions. Some dashed into Saint Patrick's. Policemen went after them, swinging nightsticks. A lean, long-haired photographer began snapping pictures of the decoy men holding down the demonstrators on the sidewalk. They were struggling again. One of the men was bleeding from a head wound. The camera snapped happily.

"Hey," shouted Chiodo, "get the fuck out of here."

232

"Get rid of that guy," growled Drackus.

The photographer danced back shouting, "I've got it, pigs! I'll have your picture in the paper tomorrow."

Chiodo grabbed the camera and smashed it against a wall.

"I'll have your badge number for this!" shrieked the photographer.

Chiodo kicked the man's feet out from under him. He scrambled up and dashed into the crowd.

"What paper's that guy with?"

"The *Village Voice*, I think."

"It figures."

Drackus, Ficelli and Bachio put the bleeding Murphy in the back of the car and roared away. Chiodo linked up with another group of TPF men confronting an advancing mob. "Here we go again," he muttered.

All restraints were gone now. Pipe-wielding demonstrators charged the TPF men, swinging the steel pipes. Policemen slashed at heads and bodies with their clubs. Finally the pressure eased as the crowds flowed northward. Radio cars and ambulances picked up the injured and rushed them away. Chiodo's squad reformed and filed back onto the bus.

The bus hissed and lurched southward. Chiodo slouched in the leather seat beside a TPF man with a bruise on the side of his face. They did not speak. Fatigue washed over him. His uniform was damp with sweat. His muscles ached. The confrontation in front of the cathedral had lasted for more than an hour, but it had seemed much longer. He closed his eyes, but his mind swarmed with visions of running hippies and shrieking mouths. He opened his eyes again. The radio calls bore a fresh urgency now. The crowds were running amok at Forty-sixth Street. And suddenly they were in the middle of it, pouring out of the bus again.

"Kill the pigs! Kill the pigs!" It was an animal roar, filling the street. To Chiodo's mind it seemed that the whole world was roaring for his blood. And what wasn't screamed from the mob came at him in crudely lettered signs: "Down With Nixon." "Down With Fascist Pigs." It happened all over again, the fighting, the screaming, the steel pipes, the running feet. By now it was night, a lurid, hate-filled night.

The pace of arrests picked up as weary policemen began seeking ways to get out of this and back to the station house. As they made their way, smashing, someone would grab a handful of hippie shirt. "You want him?" Someone would say, "I'll take him." He would go off, shoving his prisoner through the crowd. They charged groups, reformed, ripped up signs and threw them into garbage cans. Soon they were filling the buses with bodies, under arrest. Then, by one of those quirks of timing, there was a pause. Both sides backed off, breathing hard. Chiodo took off his helmet and wiped his forehead.

"Peace people, attention. Peace people, regroup. Fight the pigs! This is our revolution!"

Up the street came a van with loudspeakers mounted on its top. The van was decorated with painted flowers. A small crowd of demonstrators followed along behind it, carrying placards. "Kill the pigs!" blared the loudspeaker. "Kill the pigs!" The sound reminded him of Rushton, the Redbeard, haranguing the crowd at the Electric Circus. But this was far wilder, bloodier and more insane than that had been. If the Electric Circus had been a skirmish, this was a war. The world had gone berserk, right here on Fifth Avenue. "Kill the pigs! This is our revolution. Kill the pigs!" The van moved forward slowly, past lines of hippies and cops, and was passing in front of Chiodo. Then it happened.

A lone blue-clad figure detached itself from the ranks of a TPF squad and sprinted for the van. As Chiodo watched, frozen in his shoes, the patrolman made a diving leap at the driver's window. His arms snapped around the driver's neck in a choke-hold. The van speeded up, lurching crazily. Other cops broke from the ranks and dashed forward. The van careered onto the sidewalk and smashed into a lightpole. With a roaring rush, policemen swarmed in on the vehicle and it disappeared in a sea of blue uniforms. Nightsticks smashed out windows and headlights and beat a frenzied tattoo on the metal sides. Bodies flew from the truck, screaming. Radio equipment, seats, placards, bottles and clothing came pouring out of the mass. When the blue swarm finally backed off, the van was a battered hulk.

The incident poured new fuel into the crowd's hatred. Rioting and window smashing broke out anew. But the demonstrators' numbers had been reduced sharply by earlier arrests. Now the arrests were on a massive scale, with every available vehicle pressed into service. They shoved them into trucks, paddy wagons, buses and patrol cars and hauled them away like cattle. At 10:30 P.M. Chiodo made his last in a long series of arrests—but this one would have his name on it.

The boy could not have been over 16. He came rushing out of the dwindling crowd waving a placard and shouting, "Kill the fucking pigs. Kill 'em!"

Chiodo grabbed him by the arm. "Hey, why don't you get lost, kid?"

"No," the boy shrieked. "We're gonna kill you pigs!" Eyes blazing, he swung the sign. Chiodo sidestepped and drove his fist into the youth's side. The wind exploded out of the boy, and he went down. Chiodo hauled him to a TPF bus and dumped him in. The bus was filled with prisoners. Soon after that the demonstrations sputtered out and the 30-man squad climbed into the bus with the prisoners. As the laden vehicle headed for the station, it left behind a Fifth Avenue strewn with shattered glass, broken sticks, shredded peace placards, and splotched with human blood.

There was pandemonium at the station house. To handle the huge volume of arrests, prisoners were being processed by both the 17th and 18th precincts. They waited in long lines to have prisoners photographed, more lines for fingerprinting, still more lines to fill out arrest cards. Some prisoners had been dumped into vans and buses without an arresting officer and were released on the spot. Chiodo chatted with his own prisoner, Carl Despi, and learned that the boy had no real involvement in the demonstrations, nor any strong feelings about Vietnam. He had merely been swept up in the emotionalism of the mob. Chiodo charged him with rioting and resisting arrest.

The Fifth Avenue riots shook New York City. Chiodo pondered the irony of this the following day, as hundreds of arrested demonstrators jammed the courtrooms, and the press began its painful reappraisals. Predictably there were bitter denunciations of police tactics, and rumblings of wholesale shake-ups in the department. Many of the youths carted off to jail came from families of power and influence, and pressures bore down on judges for leniency. It was all right to tear up the ghettos, Chiodo mused, but Fifth Avenue was something else again. Let the rioters burn out whole tenements in Harlem, but let not a single brick smash a window at Saks Fifth Avenue. This had been a riot not of the bitter black youths, steaming in their social deprivation, but of the privileged white middle class. And while their wrath focused on Vietnam, he felt that this served to mask deeper rebellions; and what more obvious target was there than the policeman?

Frank Murphy lay in the hospital with a brain concussion and 28 stitches in his head. But for a mixup in orders it might have been Chiodo lying there. The thought nagged at him as Murphy's attackers, one of them a husky 32-year-old avowed Maoist booked as John Sable Peak, the son of a prominent Long Island attorney, arrived at the packed arraignment hearings. While Murphy was credited with the arrest, decoy man Paul Bachio volunteered to handle the processing. Bachio promptly encountered the wrath of Peak's wife, a pale, pinch-faced girl who had been arrested among the rioters.

As the arraignment progressed, Chiodo overheard policemen grumbling among themselves about the leniency of the judges. "They're handing out twenty-five-dollar cash bonds, and seldom anything over fifty," muttered a cop with a bandaged hand. "You'd think the bastards had spit on the sidewalk." To help speed the releases the Fifth Avenue Peace Committee doled out cash at a desk in the courtroom from a large fund collected for that purpose.

Chiodo managed to push his way to the front of the crowd when Peak stepped before the judge, flanked by Paul Bachio. Peak's head was swathed in bandages, and one eye was swollen almost shut. His yellow sheet showed previous arrests on charges stemming from street riots. In the attack on Murphy he was charged with assault with a deadly weapon.

As the judge put aside the yellow sheet, Peak's wife jumped up from her seat in the courtroom. "Look at what that fucking pig did to my husband!" she shrieked. The judge seemed unruffled by the outburst.

Paul Bachio turned and glared at her. "If you don't shut your fucking mouth, bitch, you're next." He faced the judge again. "All right, Your Honor. We're ready."

The judge set Peak's bond at $3000. Paul Bachio escorted his prisoner out to the clerk's office. Chiodo followed them. The wife and mother were at the committee desk, begging for bond money. "I've got twenty-five hundred cash. It's all I brought with me," the mother was saying. "Please let us have the other five hundred."

The Peace Committee man put up his hands. "Madam, we have a lot of bonds to make today. That is rather high, you know."

"Lock him up, Paul," muttered Chiodo. "They don't have the bond money."

The mother whirled on Paul. "Didn't it give you enough pleasure to beat my son? Now you want to put him in jail too?"

"Your son's no good," Bachio replied. "He deserves to be in jail."

"It's you who are no good," the woman snapped.

"Capitalist pig!" hissed the wife.

"Mrs. Peak, we will advance you the five hundred dollars," the Peace Committee man said. "Sign here, please."

Bachio watched them leave the courthouse, shaking his head in disgust.

As Carl Despi walked free on a $50 bond, Chiodo had already made up his mind to put in a good word for the boy when his trial came up. Subsequent events confirmed that the boy deserved all the help he could get.

A skinny, dungareed girl carrying a clipboard shouldered through the crowd and looked up at Chiodo. "You are an officer, aren't you?"

"Yeah, why?"

"I would like your name and shield number."

Anger boiled inside him. "Chiodo," he snapped. "C-h-i-o-d-o. Number two-seven-nine-nine-six. You can tattoo it across your fucking chest!"

It was a mistake. A few days later he would find out just how serious a mistake. In the wake of the riots TPF headquarters was flooded with complaints of police brutality. Among those cited in formal charges was Chiodo. Three members of the Peace Committee signed statements saying he had blackjacked Carl Despi in the bus on the way to the station. Obviously the girl was a member of the Peace Committee and had asked for his shield number for identification. But when the complaint came up for a hearing the boy refused to sign it, saying the charge was untrue.

Afterward they took Joe Drackus to Killy's for a beer. The sergeant was in a somber mood. There was scuttlebutt that some of the decoys in other precincts were being reassigned. The shrewd Drackus sensed the working of departmental politics in high places. This, coupled with the lingering aftermath of the Fifth Avenue riots, dampened their spirits. An old TPF man grunted and tugged at his earlobe. "This fucking city is coming apart at the seams," he said. "We're about due for another black rampage, wouldn't you say so, Joe?"

"I wouldn't be surprised."

"You ever been in a real ghetto blowup, Chiodo?"

238

"Not a real big one, no."

"My asshole puckers just thinking about it. If you think Fifth Avenue was rough . . ."

Chiodo said nothing. He stared into his beer and forced his mind to think of other things. He wondered if anybody had ever counted the bubbles in a glass of beer.

15

Crisis Point

Routine. Why was so much of living a routine? Bank clerks had routine. Teachers had routine. Truck drivers, lawyers, salesmen and scientists had routine. The New York Police Department was shackled by routine. Even a decoy man had his routine. The riot had temporarily broken it, of course, but months had passed since then. Chiodo grumbled under his breath and finished his dinner. It was stew. Linda made good stew. As he pushed back from the table, she studied him with a worried frown. "Something wrong?"

"No, babe. Nothing wrong."

"Dinner okay?"

"Fine, fine."

He put on his old clothes and gave his desk in the den a parting glance. The part-time business was doing surprisingly well. He had gone into selling gifts and home-decorating items, sandwiching the work between classes at John Jay and work. The business was fattening the Chiodo family treasury, as evi-

240

denced by a stack of invoices on the desk awaiting his attention. Oh, well, they would wait. He glanced at the clock. Ten after five.

The girls were playing in the yard. He kissed them on the way to the car. "Catch a bad guy, daddy," said Diane.

"Okay, I'll catch a bad guy."

Maybe this evening he would grab an hour to visit one of the other precincts. He was running for one of the Patrolmen's Benevolent Association's delegate assembly seats. The TPF would elect three delegates. In the squad room they had laughed. "Chi, you ain't got a chance. Do you know what you're up against? Dominick Bonno knows everybody in TPF. He's run twice and couldn't win." He shrugged. That was Bonno's problem, not his.

Chiodo drove down the familiar street, past the line of two-family houses with their neat yards and hedges. It had turned into a cop neighborhood. On one side of him lived a cop from the 83rd Precinct; on the other a motorcycle man transferring to vice; at the end of the block was a young guy finishing the academy; on the next street lived another cop who had been a classmate in the academy. Cops. Cops and routine.

Atlantic Avenue to Woodhaven Boulevard, make a left on Woodhaven to Queens Boulevard and go over the Queensborough Bridge. Then fight traffic across town to the Fifty-fourth Street station and try to find a place to park. Yeah, just try. The Fifty-fourth Street station loomed up like an old castle. All it needed was a drawbridge and a dragon. Well, it had its Drackus. He chuckled to himself.

"What the hell are you smiling about?" It was the station security officer. Chiodo nodded and walked on. What a change a little time can bring. He remembered how it had once been, when he was new to decoy, padding in self-consciously in his tattered clothes, having to show his shield to get past the security man. Then the man's needling grin as he called to the desk lieutenant, "Hey, lou, get a load of this one. Ain't that a winner?" To the left past the desk, then a right and another right, downstairs to the basement and along the hallway with its network of ancient steam pipes, into the squad room. Why did the place always smell like a gymnasium?

And there they were, his esteemed colleagues, sitting around on the desks among the filing cabinets and musty odors, bull-shitting. "Hey, Chi, how's the big candidate? Man, I never heard of nobody running for the PBA with all them signs and posters around. You'd think you was running for mayor.

"I oughta be running for mayor. I'd do a lot better than that dumb ass we got now."

"Hey, listen to that! Being top cop for the month again ain't good enough. Now he thinks he can run the city."

The new sheets were on the bulletin board, listing the top teams in arrests for the previous month and the individual scores. "Yeah, go look at your name on the bulletin board, Chi. Right there on top. Go look at your name, supercop. Take a pitcher of it."

He rummaged through the mail for subpoenas. None. He checked the team rosters. Good, he was working with Mayhew and Blake. Behind him the talk went on. "Hey listen, Charlie, are you looking to catch tonight? No? Good. I want to go see my chick, and we'll find one for you, too. Ask Joe for a two-man team." Chiodo lit a cigarette and listened. Routine.

But he knew that the routine would be broken the moment he stepped back out through the station-house door. This was the magic of the job, always something different. You worked and learned. At any time he could summon up bizarre scraps of memory—evidence that the dividing line between man and animal could be thin indeed.

A week earlier he had been teamed with two men with whom he had not worked before. They were after heroin, and Joe Scott had made a bust previously in a Puerto Rican tenement. So they had barged into an apartment under the stairs on a return visit, frisking a middle-aged man and a younger woman.

242

Nothing. "The shit's here," fumed Scott. "I know it's in here." While Chiodo watched, Scott and his regular partner ripped open cushions, overturned the couch, ran their fingers along moldings, peered into the stove, the toilet, the closet, the dresser drawers. Nothing. Finally they had exhausted every conceivable hiding place. Scott glared at the woman, a sudden awareness in his eyes. "On your back, sister, and spread 'em." Chiodo started to grab him but was too late. The woman was down on the couch, struggling, and Scott's hand plunged between her legs. His groping fingers drew out 30 decks of heroin in a bundle slightly larger than a matchbox. "Right up the old bun," he gloated. The woman cursed him bitterly in Spanish.

You worked and learned.

The decoys were becoming unpopular in some higher echelons of command. Even the glamour publicity did not seem to curb the trend. If anything, their glowing headlines fed resentment and interdepartmental jealousies. The freewheeling nature of the decoys, which sometimes brought embarrassing incidents, did not help matters. Chiodo, Mayhew and Blake certainly had not won any points the previous month in the raid on the Puerto Rican orgy.

One could argue that they had had a bona fide complaint. A woman on the street, after all, had reported that three young girls were being held in an apartment against their will. She complained of loud noises, frequent fights and drunken singing. Chiodo had debated this in his mind as he and his partners knocked on the door of the second-floor tenement flat. From inside came curses and squeals.

"Who ees there?" a voice called.

"Hey, amigo, we want to join the party," Blake replied in his best Puerto Rican accent.

"Go away."

There were female giggles. The decoys exchanged glances. Chiodo shrugged, aimed his foot at the lock and kicked the door open. Then they stood there in astonishment.

Two adult men, two women and three young girls were in the living room, all naked. One of the young girls was on her hands and knees on the couch, and a fat, perspiring man hunched over her from behind, copulating dog-fashion. Another couple made love on the floor. Others sat drinking beer and watching.

"What the hell—"

The man on the couch uncoupled from the girl and rushed at the decoys, shouting in Spanish. Blake smacked him in the face and he somersaulted backward over a chair. Another man dashed for the kitchen. Mayhew ran after him. There was a sound of struggle in the kitchen, then two shots.

Chiodo and Blake rushed into the kitchen and found their partner standing with his revolver in hand. Writhing on the floor, his left arm shattered, was a naked Puerto Rican.

"What happened?" Chiodo shouted.

"I shot the spic bastard."

"What for?"

"Look." Mayhew pointed to a six-inch kitchen knife on the floor beside the gasping man.

"Oh, shit."

"What'd you expect me to do? The son of a bitch was going to cut my throat."

"Madre de Dios!" screamed the Puerto Rican.

"What are we gonna do?"

"Let's get out of here," stammered Blake. "They don't know who we are."

"We can't do that."

Sirens were approaching outside. Moments later half a dozen uniformed patrolmen came pouring into the apartment. As the decoy men explained, the man on the kitchen floor screamed, sobbed and prayed. "I am dying. Get a doctor. Get a doctor!"

"You'd better call your commander," a sergeant told Chiodo. "Get a boss down here."

Drackus arrived in 15 minutes, his round face etched in disbelief. As the wounded man was carried out, Drackus questioned the people. The three girls told him they were runaways from the Midwest who had arrived in New York six weeks before with no place to stay. A Puerto Rican they met in Washington Square Park invited them to the apartment. He and two other men raped them repeatedly, and an older woman had forced them to submit to lesbian acts. The crowd was always drinking and having a party. After a week the girls began to enjoy it.

The scowling sergeant confronted his men. "You busted in here without a warrant. How many times do I have to tell you guys to stay on the street. Well, you're out of the unit, out of TPF, and I'll do my damndest to get you off the force!" His fury took them by surprise.

The wounded man was taken to the hospital, and the three other defendants went to night court for arraignment. None were able to post bond and were held in custody for a hearing. After the arraignments it was a grim ride back to the station house. By now, however, Drackus's temper had cooled, and he began to see the arrests in a new light. They had the knife assailant, after all, for assault on an officer with a deadly weapon. There were morals charges against all the adults involving the girls, each of them under 16. By the 2:00 A.M. return roll call the sergeant had changed his mind. "At least we've got a story," he said. "Now as I understand what happened, you say you started to question this guy on the street, is that it? He took a poke at you, and you chased him into the apartment. So you went into the place in hot pursuit. Isn't that the way you told me it happened?"

"Uh, yeah, sergeant. That's how it was."

"Okay, then," Drackus frowned, "but you shitheads are still going to be in trouble with Sully."

When all the decoy men had gathered for the return roll call, Drackus made a speech. "The super-Sicilian here, Chiodo, and his meathead partners could be in a real jam over an incident tonight that I won't go into. But I want every one of you guys to hear this. I don't want you inside, I want you out on the street where you belong. The next incident that comes up—I don't care what your story is—and it happens inside, you're going to find your ass out of the decoy unit. This is the last time I'm going to say this!"

He stalked out of the squad room, leaving a babble of astonished voices behind. "Hey, Chi, what happened? . . . Blake, what have you guys done now? You're always getting this outfit in trouble. . . ."

They stuck to the story. The girls were taken to Juvenile Detention Hall until their parents arrived to claim them. The parents declined, however, to press charges against the men. Chiodo tried to get a conviction for endangering the morals of minors, but this was dismissed for lack of a complainant. In the aftermath of the shooting, meanwhile, reverberations were reaching higher levels of command.

"Let's go, Chi." Blake stood at the squad-room door. They walked out of the station to Mayhew's car. "What'll we do tonight? Do you want to catch?"

"Play it by ear. Let's just drive around."

It was a quiet night. As they cruised the streets of lower Manhattan, Chiodo talked about his campaign for PBA delegate. "The trouble with PBA is the organization's dominated by rubber-gun cops. Most of them have nice cushy desk jobs and good income on the side, so they couldn't care less about the problems of the cop on the street. You take these pay issues, for instance. It's not right that cops have to report for roll call fifteen minutes ahead of duty hour and not get paid for it. Yet it's always been done that way, and the rubber-gun guys aren't going to hard-bargain for changes. The parity thing, too, sticks in a lot of craws. The sergeants got their raises, and now the city is trying to screw us out of ours."

"Well, what the hell's all this strike talk, then, if it ain't hard bargaining?" Mayhew said. "I never heard of New York City cops even thinking about going on strike before. Sickouts, yeah, but not a full-fledged strike. Yet there's plenty of talk about it now."

"They did it in Montreal, Pat, and the bad guys had a field day. That cop strike cost millions of dollars and took several lives."

"I still say it ain't right, cops going on strike," Mayhew grumbled. "That's like doctors going on strike."

"Quiet, you guys. The radio."

The call was to all TPF units. "Attention. Attention. TPF officer shot. Need A-positive blood. All TPF members with A-positive blood report to the Jewish Memorial Hospital, a Hundred and ninety-sixth and Broadway. Attention, all TPF units . . ."

"That's the Fiftieth Precinct," said Blake. "What's a TPF guy doing in the Fiftieth Precinct?"

"Damned if I know, but let's roll," said Chiodo. "I've got A-positive blood."

Mayhew whipped into a U-turn at Seventh Street and Third Avenue, burning rubber. They hit the West Side Highway and roared north. In his haste Mayhew almost made a wrong turn onto the George Washington Bridge. "Hey, meathead, that goes to New Jersey!" They bounced over a traffic divider, swerved from the path of another car and got back into a northbound lane.

"I can't figure out how a TPF guy got shot way up there. I never heard of TPF being assigned there."

Chiodo radioed TPF headquarters. "Was that message correct? The officer was in the Fiftieth Precinct? Kay."

"Affirmative."

A few blocks from the hospital they stopped at a light, and a bearded man in another car called to them. "Can you please give me directions to the Jewish Memorial Hospital?"

"Follow us. We'll take you there."

As they pulled into the parking lot and jumped out of the car, the other driver hurried into the emergency entrance with them. "I'm a rabbi," he said. "I was called about an officer shot."

A sergeant stood in the waiting room. He answered their questions. "The man was working his day off up here in the Five-oh. The way we got it, he was walking past a liquor store and two holdup men came charging out. They saw the uniform and just opened up on him. He got some shots off, too, before he fell, and the liquor-store owner came out with a twenty-two and peppered the getaway car. It was a blue Pontiac."

"How bad is he?"

"We don't know yet. He's in surgery. Stand by."

A doctor came out half an hour later. By then the waiting room was packed with TPF patrolmen and decoys. There was no immediate need for Chiodo's blood.

"He'll be all right," the doctor told the sergeant. "There were three bullets in him. We got two of them out. The other is lodged next to his spine, and we had to leave it."

It was remarkable how TPF men managed to survive. Over the years they had been shot, stabbed, stomped and beaten, but no man had died in the line of duty. A decoy man, Kenny Markowitz, had even been hacked with a machete when he stopped at a gas station on his way home from work in Brooklyn. Two black attackers had mauled him, slashing savagely at his arms, face and hands, severing one ear and leaving him for dead in his car. But somehow, even though he was never to be the same man again, Kenny had lived.

"The luck of the TPF," Mayhew said as they drove back to lower Manhattan. "It's just plain, dumb luck."

In the weeks that followed, Chiodo bore down with his PBA campaign. He visited TPF units in Manhattan, Brooklyn, the Bronx and Queens and spread his leaflets and posters through the station houses with the slogan "Vote for the Cop on the Street." When the balloting finally came, voting spread over four nights in order to give every possible man a chance to

248

express his preference, including those coming back from days off. Of the eight candidates for three seats, the top man drew 394 votes, Chiodo was second with 349, and the third man elected received 280. In the squad room the snickers and jokes were stilled.

"How the hell did you do it?" said an astonished Charlie Ficelli.

Chiodo grinned. "If you want something bad enough, you've got to go after it."

Now the PBA activities were added to all the others. In meetings and conferences Chiodo began learning to think on his feet. He had won a voice. Among the 380 delegates it was a small voice indeed, but better than none at all. He found that other policemen—precinct cops, detectives, men in vice and narcotics—shared many of his discontents over pay, working conditions and prestige. Narcotics men grumbled over the city's refusal to provide money to make drug buys. "If you've got a big bust working that requires a bundle of cash," complained one long-haired narcotics man, "forget it. You've even got to dip into your own pocket to buy a four-dollar deck, and just hope you'll get it back when you've made the collar." But the biggest source of rancor was pay: uncompensated overtime and parity increases for the lower ranks. Feelings ran so high that some men were on the verge of open rebellion.

"Hey, Chi, some decoys in Brooklyn are in hot water."

"What do you mean?"

"Something about a bribe. Ten grand. It's really hitting the fan. One of the guys is supposed to have made a fantastic number of collars. Name's Windom."

"Windom?"

"Yeah. They call him 'The Wind.'"

"Well, I'll be damned."

Since his experience with The Wind two years before, Chiodo had avoided the icy-eyed dynamo, but reports had filtered back from time to time. The Wind had gone into a Brooklyn decoy unit and kept up his fanatical pace of arrests. There had also been a report of a shooting incident in which a black man was killed, but Windom and his partner Ted Brisket had come through unscathed. As Chiodo heard the story, the decoys had made a car stop in plainclothes, a violation of TPF rules. A man and woman were in the car. The man had come out of the driver's side with a gun in his hand. Brisket started shooting. As the gunman tried to flee, both decoy men blazed away until he fell in the street. A crowd poured out of a nearby black bar. The woman dashed from the car and flung herself, sobbing, across the body. Windom and his partner, meanwhile, started arguing loudly over which of them had fired the fatal bullet. "I killed him!" raged The Wind. "No you didn't," retorted Brisket. "I killed him." Luckily a radio car arrived before the crowd got out of hand. A routine investigation was made, and the shooting was ruled justifiable. Now, Windom was in the thick of things again.

One of the PBA's functions was to monitor investigations of charges brought against patrolmen. Chiodo interviewed the decoys as a delegate, to familiarize himself with the case when the time came to sit in on formal departmental hearings.

"Hey, man, it's a lie. A lie, man. That punk's lying in his teeth." Patrolman Windom had lost none of his hyperactive energy. The words rushed at Chiodo from the thin mouth. The Wind's eyes glistened, and he had lost weight. He seemed even paler than before. Chiodo spent two hours with him and then interviewed the two partners who had also been brought up on bribery charges. One of them, Bobby Gomart, was a quiet, slow-thinking man who had won the police Medal of Honor for heroism a few years earlier when he had shot to death a mob assassin in a wild gun battle at a train station. At the time he had been working as a Transit Authority policeman. His record in the TPF was good. The other partner was O'Hara, a sandy-haired Irishman who seemed reluctant to talk.

As Chiodo pieced together the incident, the decoy men had collared a youth carrying five decks of heroin. As Windom and

O'Hara questioned the prisoner, the boy had said, "Look, my uncle is a big man. He's got a lot of money. He'll be glad to give you guys five, even ten thousand not to bust me. I'll call him up." They arranged to meet the uncle in Prospect Park. Gomart insisted to Chiodo that he knew nothing of the bribe, but had been told by his partners that the boy was going to turn in a pusher. They waited at the park for more than an hour and, when no uncle appeared, started to leave. Suddenly a station wagon made a U-turn and cut off the decoy car. The occupants of both vehicles leaped out, guns drawn. Several shots were fired before the other men identified themselves as detectives from the 78th Squad. The uncle was in the station wagon.

"We didn't realize you guys were decoys," one detective said nervously. "This guy reported his nephew was kidnaped."

The uncle, a stocky, frightened little man, jumped out of the station wagon pointing a finger at the decoys. "Those guys tried to shake me down. They wanted ten grand not to arrest the boy."

The three decoys were taken into custody along with their prisoner. At the station, Windom screamed his denials and heaped abuse on the detectives. The desk lieutenant refused to permit the decoys' arrest. The Wind tried to charge the uncle with bribery. This, too, was rejected.

At a hearing before the commissioner's investigating board, the CCIB, Windom burst into tears. "I've been a good cop. A good cop. Look at all the arrests I've made! The louse is lyin', sir. Lyin'." Windom was given five days' suspension and transferred to uniform duty in the 78th Precinct, where the incident had occurred. Gomart and O'Hara were also put back in uniform and transferred to another precinct.

For The Wind it was the beginning of the end. Within two years Patrolman Windom would be arrested by federal narcotics agents for selling heroin. He would become a fugitive from justice for a short time and ultimately draw a five-year prison term.

Chiodo was saddened. After filing his PBA investigative report he told Mayhew, "The poor bastard was sick, Pat. And the sorry part of it is, he took two good cops down with him."

Other worrisome things also were happening. Joe Drackus, Paul Bachio and Charlie Ficelli were summoned before the grand jury to explain their part in the beating of John Sable Peak during the Fifth Avenue riots. Word also circulated that Drackus was about to be promoted to lieutenant, which meant that he would leave the decoy unit. But the worst development concerned the future of the decoy units themselves.

They were being disbanded. Quietly and without fanfare, men with low arrest totals were being shifted out of units in Brooklyn and Queens and sent back to regular TPF uniform duty.

Chiodo and his partners first heard of the changes one evening when they ran into a former Brooklyn decoy, now clean-shaven and walking a post in Manhattan. "It's happening, man," he told them. "Your days are numbered. They're phasing out all the units."

Within a few weeks the Brooklyn decoys ceased to exist as a unit, the Queens decoys were on their way out and men with low numbers were being reassigned from Manhattan North. In Manhattan South the number of men on the street each night was reduced from 18 to 12. In the squad room they peppered Drackus with questions.

"What's going on, sarge? What the hell are they trying to do to us?"

"It looks like the outfit's going down the drain," Drackus replied. "But it might not be as bad as it seems right now. The way I hear it, they're thinking about forming a new outfit, separate from TPF. We'll be treated as an individual unit with permanent assignment. You guys with the high numbers won't have to worry."

All this provided a bleak backdrop for Drackus's appearance before the grand jury. Ironically, it coincided with the formal announcement of his promotion to lieutenant. Chiodo was turned away at the door of the grand-jury room. In the late afternoon Drackus, Bachio and Ficelli joined him at Fellini's, an Italian restaurant near the courthouse. The boss of the decoys was depressed. "They're treating us like criminals," Drackus grumbled. "You'd think it was the TPF that did the rioting."

They tried to cheer him up by celebrating his promotion. Several other decoy men drifted in, shouting, "Hey, lou, congratulations!" They were joined by the TPF's genial Captain George McDonald. Ruddy-faced, with a shock of white hair and a perpetual cigar in his mouth, McDonald was a favorite of the men. He was held in special esteem by Joe Drackus, who regarded the captain as a model of what a commander should be: fair, tough, unquestionably honest and yet likable and gentle with subordinates.

By seven o'clock the drinks were buzzing in half a dozen heads and the talk had turned into a critique of the police department. McDonald was confessing that with 11 children at home he disliked the rigors of TPF duty and often thought of finding a quiet station house to work out his retirement. "I'm getting a little old for this crap."

Chiodo glowered over his scotch and bemoaned bitterly the grand jury's probe of complaints against the police. "It's all right if cops get the shit kicked out of them, but don't lay a hand on the creeps that do the kicking. Send your bleeding buddy to the hospital and then bring the bastard who swung the steel pipe before some judge who's going to pat him on the head and apologize for inconveniencing him."

Captain McDonald did not share Chiodo's chagrin. The system, he said, was designed to monitor the actions not only of the citizen violating the law but also the officer making the arrest. "Nobody's immune, Chiodo. The way the rules are written in this department, you can always be caught doing something wrong. The hardest-working, best cop on the job can get caught at something, on any tour of duty."

"Yeah, well you just try to catch me doing something wrong, captain," Chiodo retorted. "Just try. Impossible."

"Listen, in five minutes I could catch you—"

"You're fulla shit!"

"Knock it off, Chi. Don't give the captain a bad time. He's one of the best bosses on the job. He's just telling you how it is, man."

Another hour passed. Chiodo was drunk. He knew he was drunk. The faces around him were familiar but no longer clearly distinct. His mood darkened even more. The scotch left a fuzzy taste in his mouth. The voices rose and fell, irritating him. Then he was making another speech. "Fuck all bosses. Fuck all captains. Fuck all lieutenants. Fuck all sergeants. None of 'em are any damn good." He glared at Captain McDonald.

Drackus grasped Chiodo by the arm, pulled him to his feet and steered him toward the door. "You crazy guinea, get the hell out of here and go home. You're picking on the nicest guy in the department. Go home and sleep it off."

Chiodo stumbled out. "Okay. Screw you. Everybody's against me. To hell with all of you, the whole damn department."

Somehow he managed to drive to Killy's, where he slouched at the bar drinking more. Pete the bartender held out his hand. "How're you doing, Chi?" Chiodo shoved him backward into a rack of glasses. They left him alone. Then some of the decoy men arrived from Fellini's. "This drunken guinea's stupid," one of them said. "What's wrong, Chi, you ain't kicked any heads lately? You gotta pick on Captain McDonald?"

"I'm sick and tired of this job," he muttered. "The decoys ain't for long, the whole damn TPF ain't for long. I'm sick and tired of all this shit and I'm sick and tired of you guys."

"Go home."

He went. Later, his memories of the drive to Queens would be foggy. He woke up the next morning feeling terrible. The light from the windows hurt his eyes. Linda was standing beside the bed with a cup of black coffee.

"I guess last night the street wasn't big enough for you to park on," she said.

"How's that?"

254

"You parked on the sidewalk."

Things were not the same in the squad room. Joe Drackus was transferred to Rockaway Beach as a desk lieutenant. His replacement, Sergeant Bob Eller, was an eager, collegiate type with a passion for administrative order and proper paper work. Fresh from TPF uniform duty, Eller was ill at ease with his unorthodox new command, and the decoys were ill at ease with him. Morale sagged.

In the Patrolmen's Benevolent Association, meanwhile, the long-simmering pay issues were coming to a head. Two years earlier the dispute had brought a brief epidemic of "blue flu" as large numbers of patrolmen staged a sickout. Now there were bitter denunciations in PBA meetings of the city's failure to meet the terms of its contract. Although the salaries of patrolmen were supposed to be maintained at within three to three and a half percent of sergeant's pay, the sergeants had received raises that boosted their salaries as high as $14,235 per year. A two-year pay boost for patrolmen gave them only $1300 more per year, up to $10,950.

Hard-core delegates clamored for a strike, and their mood spread widely through the 28,000-member police department. Despite the state's Taylor Law forbidding strikes or work stoppages by public employees, rank-and-file policemen voted nearly three to one in a PBA referendum to force the city to terms. Militants saw the vote as a strike mandate. Old-line cops were appalled at the idea of a walkout. PBA leaders took a moderate view. Chiodo also found himself in the middle of the road. "I don't want to strike," he told a group of fellow delegates, "but I don't want to be pushed around by the city either."

At City Hall the pressure was building. Mayor Lindsay argued that to meet the patrolmen's demands would cost the city an additional $67 million a year and require similar raises for firemen and sanitation workers. The parity fight, he warned, would become an endless cycle of pay raises, driving the city into bankruptcy.

Leaders of the strike faction had many precedents to follow, going back half a century. The Boston police strike of 1919, for example, left that city stripped of protection for two bloody days while mobs ruled the streets, pillaging and raping. In the wake of that strike, a stern pronouncement by the Massachusetts governor, Calvin Coolidge ("There is no right to strike against the public safety by anybody, anywhere, any time") ultimately would catapult him into the White House.

Even as New York's crisis loomed, "blue flu" epidemics had struck other cities and towns throughout the United States, including Detroit and Pontiac, Michigan, Youngstown, Ohio, Newark, New Jersey, Gary and Marion, Indiana, and even Key West, Florida. Everywhere policemen were demanding better pay for work now fraught with rising perils. In Shreveport, Louisiana, the national president of the 150,000-member Fraternal Order of Police called for a nationwide two-day walkout to let the public "find out what it would be like if there were no police departments." Fortunately no one took him seriously.

Chiodo was swept up in turbulent scenes as the crisis reached its peak in an explosive meeting of the assembly at the Hotel New Yorker. While newsmen clamored outside the closed doors, debate raged over the meaning of the referendum. The PBA president insisted that the vote was not a strike ultimatum but intended merely as an expression of rank-and-file sentiment. This triggered an uproar between factions. Chiodo strode to the microphone with an idea for bridging the gap. "I move that we give the city a definite deadline to come up with the parity pay. If they don't, then at midnight on the thirteenth of this month every unit of the New York City Police Department will report sick except those required for emergencies." The move got the PBA president out of an impasse and, with some modification, was approved by the assembly.

The prospect of a police strike chilled Chiodo. At home he made arrangements to send Linda and the girls to New Jersey and told his parents, "You'd better get out of town, too."

256

"You guys will never go on strike," his father replied.

"Yeah, that's what we thought about the sanitation men, too, but you guys struck. We were up to our ears in garbage. Do you realize what it will be like in this city without police protection?"

John Chiodo stood firm. He had no intention of leaving.

Behind the scenes, secret borough headquarters were being established where PBA delegates could live and avoid arrest under the Taylor Law. As the deadline neared, plans also were completed for a skeleton force to work during the emergency.

On the morning of the 13th Linda woke him early. "There's a cop here," she said. "He told me to get you up."

An old precinct patrolman stood in the living room with a paper in his hand. "Sorry to do this, kid, but I gotta give you this." It was a court order forbidding the walkout, copies of which were being delivered to all PBA delegates. Chiodo read it quickly.

"You want a cup of coffee?" he said.

"No, thanks, the boss is outside. Just let me tell you, kid. Fuck the city. Strike."

The patrolman walked out to a civilian car sitting in front of the house with its engine running. Chiodo's eye caught a flash of sergeant stripes in the car. The old patrolman turned and waved. "Remember what I said, kid," he shouted. "Fuck the city. Strike!" The car drove away.

But the restraining order headed off the walkout. Later that day the delegates voted 234 to 90 to postpone the action and continue their fight through the courts. The strike crisis passed. But for Chiodo a new crisis emerged.

The remaining Manhattan South decoys were ordered back into uniform.

Sergeant Eller gave them the word at roll call. "Well, guys, it's happened. Tomorrow night's the last for decoy. After that you report back to your permanent squads in the bag. Inspector Sullivan wants us all cleaned up, hair cut, shaves, the works."

"It ain't possible, sarge. They've got to be kidding."

"They're not kidding."

That night there were no decoys on the street. They gathered at Killy's and drank away the evening. Chiodo's disappointment bordered on nausea. Mayhew tried to cheer him. "Listen, Chi, when they get the new unit organized it's gonna be even better, believe me. We'll have permanent assignment, and there won't be any of this temporary shit."

Blake listened glumly and shook his head. "You're hoping for a miracle."

"They're screwing me up in more ways than one," Chiodo grumbled. "I've got classes every afternoon at John Jay. How the hell am I supposed to get from there, at four thirty, clear out to Brooklyn for roll call in uniform at five forty-five? No way." It was silly to think about classes, but his mind was grabbing at everything. What was such inconvenience compared to the awful prospect of going back into uniform, walking a post night after night, taking his meal at nine, writing in the memo book, waiting on street corners for a sergeant to come by and make the scratch, arguing with merchants over parking tickets? Chiodo downed another scotch, neat.

They did not work on the final night either. Again, it was Killy's, and this time they persuaded a reluctant Sergeant Eller to come along for a drink. "Just one, sarge. For old times' sake."

Eller perched on the edge of his chair, fiddling with his watch. "I've gotta get back, guys. Somebody might be looking for me. Gotta get back."

"Okay, okay, let's go." Drunkenly they steered the sergeant to Chiodo's car. Blake and Mayhew piled into the back seat. Chiodo headed east. It took five blocks for Eller to realize they were not going to the station.

"Hey, Chiodo, I've got to go back to the station. Come on, fellas, quit kidding. Take me back to the station."

"Don't worry about it, sarge."

Eller protested all the way to Queens. He was still protesting as they walked into Chiodo's house and poured fresh drinks. An hour later, amid the joke telling and loud laughter, he was almost frantic.

"Look, you can't kidnap your own sergeant! I'm going to call the house, get a car out here."

"Okay, okay, sarge. We'll take you back."

At eleven o'clock, Sergeant Eller leaped from Chiodo's car and sprinted into the station house. A bleary-eyed Blake belched loudly as they drove back to Killy's. "The son of a bitch didn't even say thanks."

The 2:00 A.M. return roll call was a circus. Drunken decoy men stumbled into the squad room singing bawdy songs, arms flung over each other's shoulders. Eller counted the shaggy heads and, when all were accounted for, made a hasty departure. Ficelli suggested they punch holes in a partition with their fists. When this had been done, Blake said, "Let's shoot up the place." Grinning happily, he drew his pistol and aimed for the bulletin board.

"Hey, listen, there's all kinds of bosses upstairs!" shouted Chiodo. Blake giggled. The pistol swung toward the ceiling. "No, you dumb bastard!" The pistol wavered, slowly descended and returned to its holster. They all gave a sigh of relief.

Chiodo made his way unsteadily out of the station house, thinking, Tomorrow. There was something he had to do tomorrow. Now, what was it? Oh, yeah.

Tomorrow he had to go to the barber.

16

"Don't Make Waves"

At the age of 22 Patrolman Eddie Floyd obviously was fresh out of the academy: hair close-cropped, a ramrod in his back, nervousness in his eyes. His uniform was crisp and fresh, his leather stiff and new. Chiodo grunted. A winner. A lousy Post Three in a lousy 78th Precinct on a lousy street in Brooklyn and they put him with a winner.

"Do you think we'll make a collar tonight? I sure would like to get a collar. What do you think, Chiodo?"

"Forget it, kid. Don't screw around making collars. This is a deadbeat precinct anyhow. You just stand out here for twenty years, keep your nose clean and take your pension. To hell with collars. The city of New York don't want us to make any collars."

"But you were in decoy. All the guys were talking about that in the academy. You got more collars than anybody in Manhattan South, or almost anybody. They said you could smell a collar before you even made it."

Chiodo was irritated. For an hour they had been marching off the six blocks of Post Three in a mixed neighborhood of Puerto Ricans, blacks and some poor whites. Six blocks this way, six blocks that way, half an hour each direction. In eight hours that would be how many trips back and forth? Eight? No, seven. Meal at nine o'clock. And twice they would wait for Sergeant Allen to come by and make the scratch. If he walked this post for 17 more years, how many trips would that be? How many scratches? Well, 35 trips each way in a week and 35 scratches, times 52. No, subtract vacation . . .

"What was it really like in decoy, Chiodo? They say you guys were really loose, man. Was it a lot of fun, huh? Lots of action?"

"It was a lot of fun. There was lots of action."

The kid chattered like a magpie. "Boy, I wish they would reactivate decoy. I sure would like that."

"Get smart, kid. Don't get your hopes up. Don't make collars and don't make waves."

"I don't believe a decoy man is talking that way."

"Ex–decoy man, kid. Ex-decoy. There ain't no more decoy. What's past is past. What the hell did I get out of it? I got Post Three in the 78th Precinct, and I got you."

"Aw, it shouldn't be like that. Even if you didn't get everything you wanted, you've still got to protect people and do your job."

"I am doing my job," Chiodo replied sarcastically, "by standing here like a scarecrow. Just shut the fuck up, kid. If you want a collar, go get a collar."

"I just want to see how you do it. I hear you're the greatest on junk, man. I hear you can sniff out guys with junk."

"So can a trained dog."

He brooded. The Brownsville riots had been six weeks ago, and that had been his last collar. Six weeks without a collar, walking posts from six to two, breaking in rookies, alternating as the sergeant's driver and each afternoon dreading to go to work.

If there had been a last straw, it had to be the Brownsville riots with all their frustrations. Even the memories of them made his stomach churn.

Trouble had been boiling in the Brownsville section of East New York. All evening the 55th Squad had been on standby in Brooklyn's 88th Precinct west of the tense ghetto area. As reports of sporadic violence intensified, men had found themselves chain-smoking, or demolishing packs of gum. Chiodo had steered RMP 5317 onto DeKalb Avenue and followed the flow of traffic, listening to radio calls and wishing that Brownsville would take its smoke and go away. Mitch Bennett was riding with him then, offering small talk to ease the tension.

"This beats walking post, Chi. Cigarette?"

"No, thanks, Mitch. If I smoke much more I'm gonna have to buy an asbestos mouth."

"It's a hell of a time for the sergeant to knock off early, with a night like this ahead. How come he knocked off early, Chi?"

"He's got range in the morning, eight o'clock. He said for me to stay with the car and take along whoever I wanted, so I figured old Mitch wouldn't mind getting off his feet for a while."

"Thanks."

"That's okay."

Mitch Bennett studied Chiodo. "Finally whacked off your Fu Manchu mustache, I see. Got the hair trimmed a bit around the ears, too. Very sporty."

"Balls. It was getting to be a federal case. Sergeant Allen's screaming, 'Dammit, Chiodo, you ain't supposed to have that silly-ass Chinese mustache. You know what a regulation mustache is supposed to look like. You're not in decoy anymore, so get that brush trimmed right and them sideburns shortened. No hair over the ears. No hair over the ears.' So what the hell, I went back to the barber. The sergeant's still not satisfied, but at least he stays off my ass."

"You going to be his driver full time?"

"Part time. It's a drag, playing chauffeur, but at least I don't have to walk post every night. I'd go out of my mind walking post every night. I've got to say this for LeGrande Allen, though, he's sympathetic. All the old decoy men are having a bad time readjusting to the bag. I hear some of the guys are quitting, just telling them to shove it and walking out."

"What about you?"

"I don't know yet." Chiodo pulled up to a stoplight and waited for it to change, fingers drumming on the steering wheel. The radio brought a new flurry of reports. A fire engine was in trouble in the Seven-three. They were throwing rocks at the firemen. A precinct car was dispatched.

The top of the sun's rim slid down behind a line of buildings and was gone. The light changed and they were moving again.

"I've got a business that's doing well. I don't know what I'll do yet. If they activate the decoys again, or something similar, there's no problem. But this other shit I can't see. Maybe I'm just too much of a renegade, but working out retirement in the bag for another seventeen years isn't my idea of the good life."

They listened to the radio calls. Things had been tense now for two days. All the previous evening the 55th Squad had been on standby, too, but never called. Other TPF units had already gone into the riot area—outfits from the Bronx, Queens and even Manhattan. Now calls for reinforcements were going over the radio. A police car had been fire-bombed. Snipers were peppering fire engines in the area of Sutter and Saratoga. Whole blocks of tenements were endangered. Mobs had spilled into the streets, looting and burning.

"All TPF units in the Eighty-eighth Precinct. This is a mobilization! We have a mobilization. Attention all TPF units in the Eighty-eighth Precinct."

"That's it."

"Let's go."

Chiodo had spun the wheel in a U-turn and turned on the flashing dome light. And that had been the beginning.

For the next three nights the world seemed to have turned upside down amid screaming sirens, mobs, fire and smoke.

263

Mobs had besieged the 73rd Precinct, and only the arrival of busloads of TPF men prevented them from burning it down. And yet the standing orders had been: No arrests.

On the first night Chiodo and Bennett had prowled streets that were caught up in the madness of full riot. Windows were smashed, stores burned and looted, darting figures hurled bricks and stones. Fire engines radioed for help, their tires shot out and men scurrying for cover.

Arrests were forbidden. Tear gas was forbidden. Routine apprehension of suspects was forbidden.

"What the hell are we supposed to do, lou," Chiodo had raged at a helmeted lieutenant, "let 'em burn the fucking city down?"

"You do as you're told, Chiodo, and don't make trouble. Your job is to follow orders, not give them."

Chiodo challenged the orders in every way he knew how, even to the point of making a speech at roll call in defiance of the sergeant. On the second night, he was banished to the headquarters radio. But then, on the third night, he joined his unit when it moved into the heart of the riot area at Saratoga and Sutter. Helmeted TPF cops lined the streets, watching helplessly as jeering youthful rioters swaggered past them.

One of the militants finally caught Chiodo's eye and began to needle him. Chiodo's fury broke finally when the youth spat on him. As Chiodo lunged, swinging his club, the pent-up frustrations of all the other TPF men exploded, too. The result had been mass arrests, and a sudden end to the riots.

That had been six weeks ago. Six weeks without a collar. After that, back in uniform full time, things had settled into dull routine. He had tried to bite the bullet, swallow his resentment, fit in. But he was just not a system man. The organization was too confining, the duty unrewarding. Even the old spark among his ex-decoy friends seemed to be lost. Occasionally they met at Killy's—Chiodo, Blake, Mayhew, Banion, Ficelli and a few others—to talk over old times and speculate on the future. But old times were ancient history, and the future was filled with uncertainties. Blake chafed under the new order even more than Chiodo did, but the others seemed to be adapting gradually to life in the bag. Surprisingly some even enjoyed no longer having to expose themselves and take risks. There was something to be said for following orders and playing it safe, if you liked that sort of thing. There were men who functioned better under supervision, and men who did not. Chiodo did not. Ficelli, on the other hand, seemed to endure mainly on the promise that old decoy men would be transferred eventually into narcotics or a detective squad. These promises, however, were not yet materializing. "They ain't going to materialize, either," Chiodo said morosely.

He usually left them early now and went home. There were things to do. He was working full time each day on the sales business and earning more than his police pay. Orders and invoices were stacking up.

LeGrande Allen grappled with his difficult charge. Allen understood, for he, too, had served as a backup decoy sergeant. There had been more angry words about the length of Chiodo's sideburns. Regulations limited their length to the middle of the ear. Chiodo's sideburns extended down below the ear. When shouting failed, Allen appealed to Chiodo's sense of loyalty. "Look, I'm on your side. I understand how you feel. I've seen all this shit that's been going on and I don't like it any better than you do. But we've got young kids in the squad, and they think you're some kind of hero. So don't take it out on me." Chiodo went back to the barber for another trim, meeting the regulations at least halfway.

In an effort to be a regular fellow, Allen also had shot with the ex-decoys on the City Island police range. Chiodo boasted he could beat the sergeant using his off-duty revolver. Allen, a former pistol instructor at the academy, gleefully accepted a five-dollar bet. Then, with cold precision, Chiodo blasted a score of 278 out of the target using the small-frame .38. It was six points better than Allen's score with the regular duty revolver, supposedly a more accurate weapon. The sergeant, a frugal man, paid grudgingly. That afternoon on the trap range Allen avoided more five-dollar bets. Seven shooters pooled a dollar apiece, and Chiodo won the pot, blasting ten straight clay birds.

But you couldn't hinge a police career on trapshooting and dollar pools. A man needed more than that. He also needed more than watchman duty on a deadbeat post in Brooklyn.

"Come on, kid, let's get a soda."

Floyd nodded, drew the memo book from his back pocket and carefully wrote: "Personal, 8:15." Chiodo noticed that his penmanship was very precise.

It was a VFW building with a soft-drink machine in the poolroom on the second floor. Several blacks were shooting pool, balls clicking over the green-felt tables beneath harsh, smoky light. There was a line of sagging plastic chairs along the wall. Two bottles of Coke thumped out of the machine. Chiodo walked over to a chair, removed his cap, unpinned the shield from his jacket, took off the jacket and sat down. He drank his Coke and watched the game. Beside him Floyd stood rigidly. Chiodo glanced up at his partner and frowned. Had he been that nervous as a rookie? At the nearest table the players were down to three balls.

"I got the winner of this game," Chiodo announced.

The blacks looked over. "Sure, man."

"You're not going to shoot pool!" Floyd gasped.

"Sure, I'm challenging the table. Do you wanna play?"

"I can't," Floyd said uncomfortably. "I'm on duty."

Chiodo shrugged. "All right, you're on duty."

While the black racked the balls for a game of eight ball, Chiodo chose a cue stick and carefully chalked its tip. The black broke, laying out a broad scatter and dropping the 13 ball in a side pocket. Chiodo's eye quickly picked out two nice combination shots on the spots, and he settled into the game. Cue ball to three at the corner, kiss off the five to the side . . .

"We have to go," Floyd said. "The sergeant will be looking for us."

"Sit down, kid, relax."

A little English this time, to the right. It was a long shot to the seven in the corner pocket. The cue ball spun off to the right, hit the cushion and backed slowly to the center of the table, giving him a clean shot at the two.

"We're going to get into trouble. I can't afford trouble." Floyd scribbled something in his book. "The sergeant's probably already been around by now."

By the time Chiodo had finished his second game, Floyd was a study in abject misery. Chiodo felt a twinge of pity and put his stick back into the rack. They returned to the street an hour after leaving it. Within 15 minutes the sergeant's car was sliding to the curb. Floyd handed in his memo book, and Allen scribbled his signature and the time. The sergeant looked suspiciously at Chiodo.

"Where have you been?" Allen asked.

"We were on a personal."

"How long?"

"About an hour and a half."

The sergeant winced. "What do you mean, an hour and a half?"

"Sergeant, the book doesn't put a time limit on how long a man's supposed to spend taking a crap."

Allen told the rookie to go across the street. When Floyd was out of hearing he snapped, "Don't give me a hard time, Chiodo. I'm tired of taking your bullshit. If you've got a hard-on for the department, don't take it out on me. I'm gonna double- and triple-check you the rest of the night, and your ass had better be on post."

"Yeah, okay, sarge."

They walked again. Floyd's manner had changed. Chiodo sensed that he was no longer trusted. He did not care. Nothing would please him more than to get away from this kid, with his

267

regulation haircut, his polished leather and constant reminders of the decoy unit. Even as the thought brooded in Chiodo's mind, Floyd was back on the subject.

"Do you think they'll reactivate the decoys? What do you think, Chiodo? They look for collars, don't they? The numbers. Man, I'd like to get me a collar."

Chiodo stopped walking. "Kid, do you really want a collar?"

The eyes lit up. "Yeah, I sure do!"

"Then we're gonna get you a collar."

"What are we going to do?"

"We're gonna make car stops."

The light went out again. "Didn't you hear the sergeant at roll call a couple of nights ago? No more car stops. The order came down from Sully."

Chiodo had not heard the order. "No more car stops? TPF is known for car stops. The TPF has made more arrests checking out fishy-looking cars at stop signs than any other way. That's bread-and-butter stuff."

"Well, those were the orders. Besides, I never made one. They told us in the academy it was dangerous."

"You're damn right it's dangerous. I'm going to demonstrate for you, but listen to what I say. Ninety-nine times out of a hundred the guy's okay, but just as soon as you get careless, along comes some punk who's just held up a liquor store, packing a three fifty-seven Magnum."

"Yeah, but—"

"Don't worry about it. I don't care how many orders come down, a policeman has still got the right to stop a car with reasonable assumption that there's a violation. Just stay cool, kid."

At an intersection stop sign they checked out several cars. Chiodo showed Floyd how to approach the car properly, one patrolman on each side for mutual coverage. "Make sure his hands are clear when the door comes open. Make him shut off the ignition, too. That way he can't floorboard it on you and take off."

268

As they checked licenses and registrations Chiodo also demonstrated how to take a quick look under the seat without actually searching with his hand. "You're not supposed to put your hand under there. So you drop your memo book on the floor, see, and look under the seat when you bend down to get it. That's where your partner is real important, because with your head down like that he's your only cover."

Quick searches also could be made, Chiodo went on, while the officer ostensibly checked the vehicle identification number. "On the old models the VIN tag is on the frame of the driver's door; in new cars it's on the molding where the dashboard and windshield meet."

An old Plymouth chugged to a stop at the intersection. The driver was a long-haired youth with a stubble of whiskers and straggling mustache. Chiodo's inner alarm clicked. "Okay, kid, we might have something here." Casually he inspected the driver's license and registration. The driver seemed nervous. Chiodo bent over to jot down the VIN from the door molding and dropped his memo book at the driver's feet. "Oops, sorry." As he bent for the memo book he saw the edge of a brown paper bag protruding from under the front seat. Chiodo straightened up and put the memo book in his pocket. "All right, kid, you check out—oh, what's that?"

"What?" The driver's eyes blinked rapidly.

"That brown paper under the seat."

"It's nothing, man, nothing. Give me my license if you're through. I gotta go, man. I'm in a hurry."

"Don't make a move." Chiodo plucked out the brown paper bag and opened it. From inside came the familiar odor of dry grass. "Floyd, put your cuffs on him."

The rookie was startled. "What for?"

"Marijuana, man. The kid here's carrying a whole bagful. Put your cuffs on him."

The hippie did not resist but seemed genuinely surprised at his arrest. "Hey, man, everybody smokes grass. Hey, I bet you smoke grass, too. Don't bust me, man, this is nothing. Why don't you get some real criminals?"

Floyd was jubilant. He snapped on the handcuffs. "I got a collar," he said. "I got a collar."

Chiodo also felt the old surge of excitement as he put Floyd in the back seat with the prisoner and drove the old Plymouth to the 78th Precinct station. Soon the radio was summoning Sergeant Allen to the station house. He arrived at a brisk trot.

"Chiodo, how'd you make this collar?"

"Made a car stop, sarge."

Allen's face took on a mottled color. "No more car stops. Didn't you get the word? It came from Sullivan himself. No more car stops. No more car stops."

Chiodo laughed. "I'm just bustin' your balls, sergeant. The license plate was hanging. We thought it might be a stolen car, so we checked it out. We saw this stuff on the floor—"

"Don't give me that shit, Chiodo. I know all those tricks. You're not supposed to make any more street-corner car stops and that's it."

"Sergeant, do you mean to tell me the inspector wants us to ignore our duty? Why, that's malfeasance. It's a crime for a cop not to take action when he sees something suspicious and fails to check it out. Is that what you're telling me, sergeant, that I should look the other way?"

Allen was holding his breath. He looked at the ceiling and exhaled very, very slowly. "Chiodo, you're giving me a hard way to go." The voice was carefully controlled. "I'm going to have to do something about you. I've got to get you transferred out of my squad."

"Then get me transferred, sergeant. Go ahead. I might as well be a policewoman, the way things are now. Pretty soon they'll be taking my gun away and issuing me a water pistol."

Floyd was elated. As Chiodo wandered into the sitting room he heard scraps of conversation from a huddle in the corner where young cops surrounded his rookie partner.

"Hey, you got a collar!"

"Yeah, you ought to see this guy work. It's just like they say, he can smell junk . . ."

Chiodo strolled past them casually on his way to the toilet. He felt like whistling. But that would be overdoing it. He squared his shoulders and walked tall.

One of the rookies approached him. "Hey, Chiodo, can I get to work with you one night? Huh?"

"You want to make collars, too?"

"I sure do."

"Sure, kid, why not?"

But it could not go on. A man could not build his future playing hero to a bunch of recruits. The way up the ladder of the police department was crowded, anyhow, and he knew now that he lacked the patience to wait his turn for advancement. Too much had been packed into less than three years to settle down now, pounding a post and chauffeuring a sergeant. He was a hunter, not a guard; and the hunt was on the home ground of the game, blending into the bush and following the spoor. In uniform a man was one of the troops, his movements confined and his instincts curbed. There was little room to exercise initiative beyond the routine. It was not a question of bravery or ability; many uniformed men had both. It was a question of temperament. By temperament Chiodo found his zest in competing. This had been the true excitement of decoy work. They had competed fiercely among themselves and fiercely against the predators of the street. Something in that bizarre life had struck a primal chord; his drive had been private, uncompromising and basic. It had tested his resources to the limit, and proven things that need proving in every inner man. The decoy was more than a cop; he was a free and elusive spirit, part of the society and yet out of it, part of a huge organization and yet enjoying enormous personal power and freedom of action. Few men anywhere in the normal workaday world ever experienced such an existence, and yet all secretly hungered for a taste of it.

From now on Chiodo could sift back over those experiences

and know that many of his instincts as a man had been satisfied, while at the same time something positive was contributed to the order of society. The Aliens had given him sweet vengeance. The thwarting of the Electric Circus fire-bomb plot had probably saved scores of innocent victims from terrible agony and death. The night in Susie's pad had satisfied fantasies of a different kind. And the riots had served both to create rage and then to give vent to it. Man, after all, was innately a creature of violence, and there lurked in each of us, carefully disguised, a decoy man.

As for the system, it had a remarkable resiliency. The police, the courts, the politicians, the public—each not only possessed a vitality of its own but also an amazing adaptability to change. The corruption and inefficiency, the mismanagement and injustices would give way to pressure. A certain degree of this was not only condoned but demanded by the public. If the public did not buy crooked cops, bribe corrupt judges or condone larceny in high places it would not exist. Men with briefcases and business suits stole far more each year than men with guns. Only when the public realized that condoned corruption also fed the monster of crime in the streets—that one hand, as a Mafioso put it, washed the other—would change begin to take place.

In time, change would come about. In time the cries of the victims would grow louder than the exhortations of lawyers, and society would seek a fairer balance. One cop was not going to achieve change. One cop could chafe in his frustration until doomsday and go unheard. There were other battlegrounds, in business and politics, where a man could swing a bigger stick. There were not enough jails to hold all the street junkies, stickup men, rapists, thieves and murderers. A broader attack also had to be mounted against the system that spawned them.

Chiodo knew that he had to come to a decision. It was not something one arrived at overnight but through prolonged frustrations growing out of the job. The job had settled into a maddening exercise in futility.

In court a number of his pending cases were falling apart. The last hope of putting away the Aliens on rape charges had collapsed. In the John the Limp case, Chiodo's pleas to commit Lew, the young informer, for drug treatment went unheeded, and the boy began serving his five years. Chiodo cursed the stupid system that through bureaucratic indifference would turn a potentially useful citizen into a hardened addict and future criminal, totally soured on society. Then his own hearing had come up in the Fifth Avenue riots. For a full day he had cooled his heels outside the hearing room without being informed that his case had been postponed. His protests brought a patronizing smile to the face of the lieutenant. "What are you steamed up about, kid. You're gettin' paid for your time, ain't you?" When the hearing was convened the following day, he was subjected to a grueling cross-examination in front of a tape recorder. Chiodo walked out knowing that if the boy he was accused of beating had not testified in his behalf, he would have faced suspension, or worse.

There were galling day-to-day incidents as well. One night Chiodo and five other men of the squad were sent to the 60th Precinct in Coney Island for standby duty. Trouble was brewing among the blacks and Puerto Ricans. As the TPF men sat in the van talking and smoking, Chiodo thought back to the night he had been a raw rookie in this same precinct. The nightly carnival sounds of Coney Island drummed in his ears now just as they had then, but now the man had changed. Finally the van was summoned to 1212 Surf Avenue, where some precinct patrolmen were attempting to arrest a group of unruly blacks. As usual the females were making the most noise, screaming, "Yah, yah, white pigs. Go home, motherfuckers!"

Chiodo was tired. He had heard it all before, too many times in too many places. As they waded in to reinforce the precinct men, he shoved a black girl out of the way. She pulled back her fist to punch him. Instead of slamming her to the ground, he raised the nightstick high in front of his face, bayonet-fashion. It was a mistake. He was getting soft. For with a lunge the girl drove the stick into the bridge of his nose, laying open the skin. As blood poured down his face, another cop took the girl into custody. By the time Chiodo arrived at the station house from Coney Island Hospital with a patch on his nose, the precinct men had already decided to let the girl go.

"Why the hell release her?" Chiodo fumed.

"She's only fifteen years old. I don't want to get into that juvenile-court rat race."

"She's older than fifteen. She's lying. I'll prove she's a liar. Where did she say she lived?"

The patrolman gave him an address in Brownsville. Chiodo called the 73rd Precinct, and a car was dispatched to check the address. The report came back that it was a vacant lot.

"The building doesn't even exist!" he told a desk lieutenant. "How can you possibly let her go? I want her for assault."

"Mind your own business," the lieutenant snapped. "You TPF guys think you're fucking gods, coming in here telling us how to run this precinct. Get the hell out of here."

Fighting to maintain control of his temper, Chiodo left the station and went home. The next morning, for the first time since joining the department, he called in sick, knowing that he was perfectly fit for duty. He stayed out for three days.

Afterward there seemed to be no break from stultifying routine. Days on. Days off. Drive the sergeant. Walk post. Meal at nine. Don't make car stops. Don't make waves. One evening, in a frenzy of boredom, he launched a concerted assault on overtime parking meters. In less than an hour he wrote a dozen citations. "There!" he muttered to himself. "That'll teach you lawbreakers that TPF is on the job."

Then, with trouble sputtering again in Brownsville, his squad was put on standby alert. But they were never called into action. They spent three nights sitting on the bus, playing cards.

Finally, he had had enough.

On the night after making his decision he did not sleep well. He was up early, fixing instant coffee and dreading the day ahead. One did not cut off part of one's life without second thoughts. But by the time he walked into TPF headquarters to face an administrative sergeant, O'Brian, the second thoughts were behind him. It was September 19, 1970, and he had been a cop a little less than two and a half years.

"Sarge, I'm quitting the job."

O'Brian was busy, his face buried in a stack of paper work. "I ain't got time for your jokes, Chiodo. Can't you see I'm swamped?"

"No joke, sarge, I'm quitting the job. You owe me six weeks comp time, so I'll start it immediately."

"Dammit, Chiodo, I know you ain't quitting the fucking job." O'Brian looked up impatiently and twirled a pencil between his fingers. "Okay, make it fast. What's the gag?"

"No gag, sarge. This is for real. I'm resigning from the department effective six weeks from today. Have you got a form?"

O'Brian dug a cigar from his pocket, snipped off the end with a knife and struck a match. "You sure you want to do this, Chiodo? Hell, man, you've got a good future in the department. A man with your background is bound to make detective soon, then you can go for your sergeant's exam. The pay's going up all the time, and look at the benefits—"

"Sarge," Chiodo held out his hand, "the form."

The sergeant sighed. "Okay." He pushed back the chair and went to the filing cabinet.

Chiodo filled out the form and signed it. "I'll bring in my equipment later."

He walked out of the old station house feeling strangely depressed. It was like leaving his family. Outside, a watery sunlight filtered through the light smog of a September afternoon. Manhattan soared around him, but no longer did it have the personal intimacy he had known as a cop. The police department not only had become a way of life, he suddenly realized, it was also a shelter.

The Chevy moved into traffic.

Oh, hell. At the corner a strange cop was advancing on the Chevy. While Chiodo had daydreamed at the wheel, the light had changed and cars were backing up behind him.

"Hey, buddy," the cop bellowed, "are you gonna drive that heap or park it?"

Chiodo gave him an apologetic smile.

"Sorry, officer," he said. "Sorry."

Epilogue

The experiences of the street leave an indelible mark on a man's mind. It is for this reason, I believe, that the expression was born: once a cop, always a cop. When I left the department I was a different man than when I joined, less idealistic perhaps, more conservative and wearing a tougher crust. Living with crime day in and day out—living the realities and the frustrations of a street cop—can color a man's thinking for life. I think if more citizens shared these things our homes and our streets would be safer, our society better geared to meet the challenges of today and tomorrow.

A society in fear is not a free society. Fear and freedom can't exist side by side. If I learned anything as a cop it is that the permissive society has lofty ambitions but doesn't seem to work —not, at any rate, when you are dealing with the criminal mind. Until those who would murder us, rob and cheat us, invade our homes and disrupt our peace and pillage our young with mind-destroying drugs are curbed, this country simply isn't going to realize its tremendous human potential.

Some of my liberal acquaintances are shocked when I insist that first-degree murder should still be a capital crime, with the death penalty restored, and that in my opinion the pusher of hard narcotics, especially heroin, is guilty of first-degree murder. Since we stopped executing our worst criminals, the rate of vicious violent crime has soared. While I cannot prove that capital punishment is a deterrent to premeditated murder, my instincts as a cop tell me that it is, and I feel that the restoration of the death penalty—in the absence of a workable alternative —would prove the point. But, at the same time, the overhaul of our criminal-justice system, with better safeguards against sending innocent men to the chair or the gas chamber or the hangman's noose, must be pursued continuously. The rights of the poor, the ignorant and the friendless must weigh equally in a court of law with those of the rich and influential.

But if my own experience as a cop gave me any sense of outrage at all it was in the seamy shadow world of drugs. The drug pusher, I'm convinced, is the worst criminal walking the streets of this country today, for he preys on our youth. For a few dollars' profit the street-corner pusher peddles slavery, prostitution, insanity and death. Innocent boys and girls, trapped in the confusion of their teen years and often frustrated and adrift because of indifferent, preoccupied parents, are snared as brutally and callously as rabbits caught in the hunter's traps. The drug pusher strips them of their pride, their dignity, their hope for the future and, ultimately, of life itself.

The pusher is a monster in human form.

His crime deserves the penalty of death.

This is, I'll admit, one ex-cop's point of view. All policemen don't favor such extreme measures in dealing with the animals who stalk among us. But I'd be willing to bet that if somebody took a poll of the cops on the streets of America the results would be enormously enlightening. The same might be said of a poll among victims of violent crime, who could see capital punishment as a means of obtaining, if not a deterrent, at least a measure of vengeance.

278

The mother of a young girl who was raped, murdered and then dumped in a Florida field once wrote to newspaperman Charles Whited:

There once was a time when I, too, was opposed to capital punishment. Violent crime, you see, had always happened to someone else, not to our family. And then this happened, and the agony we have gone through is unspeakable. Each day is a torment and each night a living hell. For I know that when this murderer is caught, the greatest punishment he is likely to receive for this monstrous crime against my child and her family is life in prison. With time his torment, if he suffers any at all, will become but a faded memory, but mine will live on until the day I die. Is his life so much more precious than hers?

It is not the criminal who pays for acts of wanton brutality and murder; it is the victim, and the victim's loved ones who must live on, remembering. . . .

—Dan Chiodo